SPANNING THE MILES

A Story of Lasting Love from WWII

By

Beverly J. Graves

Thank you, I hope you enjoy.

Beverly J Graves
5/6/22

DORRANCE
PUBLISHING CO
EST. 1920
PITTSBURGH, PENNSYLVANIA 15238

The contents of this work, including, but not limited to, the accuracy of events, people, and places depicted; opinions expressed; permission to use previously published materials included; and any advice given or actions advocated are solely the responsibility of the author, who assumes all liability for said work and indemnifies the publisher against any claims stemming from publication of the work.

All Rights Reserved

Copyright © 2021 by Beverly J. Graves

No part of this book may be reproduced or transmitted, downloaded, distributed, reverse engineered, or stored in or introduced into any information storage and retrieval system, in any form or by any means, including photocopying and recording, whether electronic or mechanical, now known or hereafter invented without permission in writing from the publisher.

Dorrance Publishing Co
585 Alpha Drive
Pittsburgh, PA 15238
Visit our website at *www.dorrancebookstore.com*

ISBN: 978-1-6386-7302-6
ESIBN: 978-1-6386-7650-8

Beverly J. Graves
909 West First Street
Apt #2
Pella, Iowa 50219
641-204-2254
bevgraves@mediacombb.net

SPANNING THE MILES

A Story of Lasting Love from WWII

To: My mom and dad with love.

With special thanks to my family and my dear friends who read the draft pages and encouraged me to complete this venture.

This is just a simple love story. But it's not mine, it's theirs, Dorothy and Henry Collins. It's all about their love for each other during a time of great strife on our planet, World War II. Dorothy and Henry were not the only soldier/bride couple to marry during WWII. Thousands of European girls married American soldiers and came to the United States after the war. Like many of them, Dorothy and Henry were to be separated soon after they were married. Separated by 4,500 miles across two countries and an ocean.

As the story begins, their daughter, Barbara Grayson is sad to know that her mom, Dorothy is slipping away from her with the onset of Alzheimer's. On a warm summer day, when Dorothy says she is going to clean out the old wooden box and throw away the letters she and Henry had written to each other, Barbara asks her mom to let her have them. Dorothy is hesitant at first. She wonders why anyone would want to read them, but then grants the request if Barbara will promise not to read them until after Dorothy is gone.

Years later, when Barbara opens the packet of letters, gently tied up with string, she is overwhelmed at the intimate, passionate love her parents expressed over the long months they were apart.

Dorothy and Henry had a love that spanned the miles between England and America, that even a war and the distance could not separate. Their letters are intertwined throughout this story with glimpses of their lives before, during, and after the war. This is a story of their love, which they vowed could withstand any hardship.

Prologue

As Barbara Grayson watched her mom, Dorothy, meticulously folding clothes in her bedroom, she heard the distant sound of a train whistle coming through the open window. The crisp, white lace curtain had been starched and ironed and it rustled softly in the warm summer breeze. From the train whistle's tone, Barbara could tell it was on a track far beyond their house and the breeze gave the train whistle a forlorn echo. It hadn't sounded that way when they were kids, when the trains ran regularly on the track behind the house where Barbara grew up. The sound of that whistle was cheerful and it brought joy to their young hearts. As soon as they heard the first toot, they forgot about their current game of "Olly, Olly, Oxen Free". Bicycles were dropped in the yard and nearby neighborhood kids would start running to the far back of Barbara and her younger sister, Deanna's yard. Watching the trains pull into the watering station wasn't only a summertime treat for the Collins sisters. No one else ever missed joining in either.

In spite of Dorothy's warnings of mean old hobos running away with children never to be seen again, the neighborhood kids ignored her and would run down the backyard and wave to the train engineers and Barbara and Deanna were right there with them. Their young minds couldn't comprehend why a hobo would want to snatch any of them. They were only watching the train pulling into the watering station, albeit amidst a lot of yelling and jumping up and down to get the engineer's attention. Dorothy had always been afraid whenever a lone hobo had approached the house asking for a bit of bread or milk or any other leftovers. She just knew that they were dangerous, even though there had never been any trouble from the campsite on the railroad's right-of-way, a few yards from their house where the vagabonds spent the night. But she would quickly grab her children, take them inside and close the back door just in case.

Steam engine trains were still in use during the late 1950s and the water tower sat looming over the Collins' back yard. Most of the time it just sat there unpretentiously, watching and waiting patiently for the next train to arrive. But when the trains pulled into the watering station, the tower came to life and began its work of filling the train's parched tank. The gush of the water and steam could be heard as the train gulped to its fill. In the children's excitement, they waved, yelled, and smiled at the engineers who would blow the train whistle as it pulled to a stop. The children always thought the whistle was just for them even though it actually was a signal to the train crew of the arrival at the station.

They had learned that if they jumped, yelled and waved enough, the engineer would throw a pack of **Juicy Fruit** gum out the open window of the big steam engine. Of course, if Barbara's mom saw it, she wouldn't let them chew it. Once while she was hanging freshly washed clothes on the line she had seen the engineer toss the pack to the kids and she immediately confiscated it saying, "You don't know where that gum has been." Well, of course, they didn't know where it had been, but they could imagine lots of far-off exciting places, wherever the train traveled on its journey. Chewing the gum made them feel just a little bit part of that journey. After then, they made sure to look to see if Dorothy was hanging out clothes. If the coast was clear, they ignored her previous words of warning and quickly opened the pack and shared it with everyone. Perhaps the other mothers were not as afraid of the train engineers and hobos as Dorothy because the neighborhood kids never worried or doubted they would get a piece of that special treat. The gum tasted so good, sweet and juicy, just like its name and they savored every chew until the flavor was gone. Maybe it just tasted so good because it was a secret pleasure they shared and kept from Mrs. Collins.

When the engine had drunk its fill and the steam began to pour out of the top, the big wheels of the train began to turn and the engine chugged slowly out of the watering station onto the next leg of its mysterious journey. The engineer would wave at the children and blow the whistle. This time it absolutely was just for them and the children laughed and ran to get the packet of gum from the edge of the weeds.

Barbara smiled to herself at the memory. Even to this day, the smell of **Juicy Fruit** gum brought back sweet thoughts of those long, lazy, summer days when life was simple and her mom's freshly washed clothes were filled with the smell of sunshine from the summer breezes. Barbara could still see herself and the others as they ran down the back yard to the weeds that separated the railroad tracks from their property.

The children knew the weeds that separated their property from the railroad tracks were the forbidden area and always respected that warning from their parents. If the truth be known, it wasn't really because of the hobos, but until the City crew chopped down the weeds occasionally, they knew there might be snakes living in there. And the knowledge of potential snakes was more of a deterrent than dirty old men camping on the right-of-way. Their self-imposed barrier was where they stopped to wave at the engineer from the edge of the tall weeds. There had been a couple of times, the **Juicy Fruit** hadn't made it beyond the weeds, much to their disappointment, but venturing into the snake infested jungle was simply not done.

The Collins' property wasn't a very large piece of ground, but it belonged to them free and clear. Barbara's dad, Henry, had saved enough money to purchase the land after returning from the war and it was where he lovingly built their house. The lot was long and narrow and many summer days were spent playing racing games up and down the yard with the other neighborhood kids. Barbara's thoughts wandered again and she remembered how every Saturday morning her dad would get out the old push mower and walk its length many times to trim the grass and weeds, being especially careful not to mow over any of her mom's flowers. Henry didn't particularly care for all the flowers that had been planted in his way, but he knew how important they were to Dorothy, so he never let her know about his distaste for having to mow around them. To Dorothy, they were a little touch of an English garden like she had left behind. Often grumbling a bit under his breath, he would mow around to their small vegetable garden. He had let Dorothy plant it as long as she didn't ask him to eat any of the vegetables. He knew she had longed to have the things she had been deprived of during the war so she planted and he mowed.

Those long summer days were now part of the past.

Chapter One

The final plaintive wail of the train's whistle drifted away as it crossed the last road at the edge of town. It prodded Barbara out of her daydreams and back to reality, her childhood memories fading with the sound of the train as it made its way onto its next destination. She knew that she would have to be making some decisions soon. She was the only one left to deal with them, even though there were things she didn't really want to handle. Henry had passed away years ago and Barbara's only sibling, younger sister Deanna, had died from cancer when she was only forty-four so there was no one else. The painful decisions would be left to Barbara to handle.

Barbara watched as her mom finished neatly folding her clothes. Even though her mind was slowly going, Dorothy's pride for her home was still intact and she wanted to keep things neat and clean as she always had. She loved her little house with the red roof, the only one in the neighborhood. She had made Henry paint the concrete basement blocks a light blue-grey shortly after she had taken the exam to become an American citizen. With the white paint of the house itself, it looked very patriotic. She was proud to have become a U.S. citizen while still retaining her British citizenship.

Now, on that sunny afternoon, with the breeze rustling the curtains and the soft mournful sound of the train whistle fading, Barbara realized how the mom she had always known was fading away just like the train whistle. Barbara had been devastated when both her dad and sister had died, and now she was faced with her mom's advancing dementia. The reality of Dorothy's leaving was foremost in Barbara's mind even if the leaving wasn't physical.

Dorothy looked at the pile of folded clothes and said to Barbara thoughtfully, "I think I'll clean out that old wooden box next. There are things in there I don't need."

"Okay, Mom, but let me help you. I don't want you to throw away any papers until I look them over."

"Why?"

"They could be important, like insurance or the deed to the house. I'd better look through them first." Barbara picked up the box and placed it on the bed and started to open it.

Dorothy grabbed Barbara's hand. "Wait, I should throw away those old letters first."

"What? What old letters, Mom?"

"The ones your dad and I wrote to each other. Silly of me to keep love letters for so long."

Barbara looked at her mom in surprise. "You have yours and Dad's love letters?"

"Ummhuh." Dorothy shook her head with a detached look on her face.

"You saved them all these years?"

"Of course, didn't you save your old love letters?"

"I suppose I might have if I'd ever got any." Barbara said wistfully.

"Well, your dad wrote lots of letters."

"Dad wrote love letters?" Barbara pondered this news. It was hard to think of Henry writing love letters. Oh, Barbara knew he loved Dorothy with a passion, but to put it down on paper was something Barbara never imagined.

"Oh my goodness, yes. He was so romantic."

"Dad?"

Barbara had known about the old wooden box for many years. It had always lived behind her parents' bed and the contents were a mystery to the girls when they were young.

That box had been an exciting temptation to Barbara and her sister. It was heavy and had fasteners that could pinch your fingers if you tried to open it without approval and the proper instructions of how to do so. There were no markings on the box, it was just a square box of plain unfinished wood. At first glance, you wouldn't think of it as anything special. But it held the secrets of the world, or so their young minds imagined. Barbara and Deanna had always wondered why it lived behind their parents' bed and why Dorothy got it out occasionally. She said she had to look for important documents such as insurance papers or other legal documents, like the deed to their property, her passport, and immigration papers. It also housed old family photos and the clippings from first haircuts and first lost teeth. (You know, all those important things that could never be thrown away.) But what else was in there? The memory of it made Barbara chuckle to herself as she thought, I guess my parents never felt the need to have a bank box for storing their valuable items, that old wooden box could do the job just fine.

Whenever the old wooden box came out of hiding, Barbara and Deanna always wanted to peek over her shoulder to see all the wonderful things so carefully packed away in that mysterious box that lived behind the bed. If they begged, Dorothy would let them get a look at some of her old family pictures, but never could they touch that bundle of papers tied up with string.

"Mom, what are those?" they had asked with the curiosity of children. Dorothy would say "Oh, only some old papers, you don't need to see, so don't touch them". What were they and why were they such a secret and so important and why couldn't they even touch them? That curiosity never went away and every time Dorothy would get the box out from behind her bed, Barbara and Deanna would be right there to try to see what was in it.

Barbara hadn't given much thought to the bundles tied up with string for years, but now the idea of her mom throwing away love letters seemed preposterous.

Barbara knew that Dorothy had never believed in keeping worthless items that just took up space. Only the things which were really needed were important for her to keep. She always said, "There just isn't room in this small house." So it didn't seem unusual that she would think about cleaning out the old wooden box. She had been going through several moments in recent months when she felt the need to clean out and dispose of items in the house. She had always been organized, but now the dementia had triggered something quite different. It wasn't unusual for Barbara to stop by the house and notice things missing. Clothing items, spoons and forks, the TV remote, the cordless phone, and even Dorothy's tooth bridge had disappeared. Those items never reappeared and when asked, Dorothy never seemed to know where they had gone or even knew that they were gone. She would look around with a blank stare and a shrug and say, "I must have been cleaning." So the idea of disposing of items in the old wooden box didn't seem strange to her. Just another cleaning project.

Barbara begged her, "Oh, mom, please don't get rid of the letters. Why would you want to do that? I would like to have them."

"No, no one can read them; they're mine," Dorothy said with her own wistful look on her wrinkled face. The face that had always looked so young and interested in life, now just looked old, tired and vague as she drifted in and out of that private world brought on by the dementia. It was a world that only Dorothy knew, although Barbara had sincerely tried to understand. With the little wistfulness of her own Barbara pleaded again, "Mom, let me have them. I would love to read them."

Shaken out of her private thoughts, Dorothy angrily snapped, "What? No, those are personal between me and your dad. You can't have them!"

Over the past few months it had been hard for Barbara to get used to her mom's personality change from the fun loving, energetic person who rode her bike with the grandkids, loved to swim, loved to play cards and Scrabble, and never passed up a chance to sing and dance. Singing in the church choir and doing country line dancing with the ladies' exercise group at church had been a joy for so many years, but now was no longer a part of her life. Dorothy had loved the music and dancing and she faithfully rehearsed every week. But, when it became too difficult to learn the dances and the songs, she quit going to the dance rehearsals and programs. Eventually, the church choir rehearsals became fewer and far between and finally the church service itself was forgotten. For her to not have an interest in those things anymore was unbelievable to Barbara. How could she give up those activities that had been so important to her? Of course she didn't give them up—the Alzheimer's did.

So while it was painful to hear that sudden change to an angry voice, Barbara was careful not to upset her mom any further when she replied, "Because, it would be wonderful to learn about you and dad when you were young and in love". Anger gone, Dorothy just looked at her daughter with a quizzical stare.

When Henry had died almost thirty years earlier from a brain tumor, Barbara felt she had missed out knowing him. She had fond memories of him growing up. He had been an important part of her life then and as a young adult, even though he had left them far too early. She thought maybe by reading their letters, she would have more insight of who they were when they were young, if only her mom would let her keep them.

"Please, Mom, don't throw them away. Let me have them," she asked again.

"Why would you want them? They don't mean anything to you."

"Of course they do, Mom."

Dorothy's eyes glazed over as she again wandered into the memory. "You know we wrote the first ones when your dad went to France at the end of the war."

"I know; you told me."

"After we were married he was shipped home to America. The war ended but I couldn't come with him. It was almost a year before we saw each other again."

"That must have been hard."

"It was; we missed each other so much. But, I didn't want to think about leaving Mam either. We were so close and the longer I was away from Henry, the less I wanted to come to America."

"Did Dad know that?"

"Oh, no, I never told him. I guess I thought he knew how much Mam meant to me. Of course, I did love your dad and wanted to be with him. It's just that I was young and didn't really realize how far away America was from Leicester."

"I know Mom."

"I would have brought Mam with me if I could have, but your sisters were little then and still in school. You know your granddad was never good to Mam. He was tight with his money and only gave her the bare necessity for the house. It was so hard during the war."

"I don't know how she did it."

"That's why I wanted to bring her with me to get away from him. She said all he ever wanted of her was her wifely duties; just like all men want. She said she hoped that Henry would be different for me and I suppose he was most of the time." A soft sweet look had come over Dorothy's tired face. She was back in the past. Barbara gently tried to get her back to reality.

"Let's finish the laundry, Mom and get to sorting out the box. It would mean a lot to me, Mom, to have the letters. They're special memories of you and dad when you were young. I don't want you to throw them away. Let me keep them for you."

"I don't know. I should ask your dad if he minds."

"Mom, he's gone now. It's been a long time." Barbara knew that dementia patients don't need to hear the truth and it was best to just go along with her mom, so she quickly corrected herself, "But, if he was here, I'm sure he wouldn't care if I kept them."

Dorothy looked at Barbara and hesitantly said, "I suppose it would be okay; if you're sure your dad doesn't mind."

"I'm sure, Mom."

"But they are only for you to read. They are personal and special to me, but no one else would be interested. And promise me you won't read them until after I'm gone," was her last admonishment. "We can just leave them in the box for now."

Barbara faithfully kept her promise to wait until after Dorothy's death to untie the bundle, although it was not so much to keep the promise, as it was just too hard to read them. It took her six years to finally read their letters after Dorothy passed away. The old wooden box had been brought to Barbara's home and sorted through to get important documents, but the bundle of letters had remained with the string lovingly tied in a bow. When she decided to read them, she started with her dad's letters first and tears filled her eyes and her heart broke at the intense feelings he had for Dorothy. He poured his heart out in every word. They were so young, in love, and separated from each other by an ocean and across the land on the other side of the world.

My Dearest love, I was going to wait until I heard from you before I wrote, but I just couldn't wait any longer. It's like a morgue around here, too quiet to enjoy it. I don't know what to do with myself. I got some comic books, but I'm not enjoying reading them. I love you, God, how I love you. I didn't think I would miss you quite as much, but I do. I can't seem to think right and I've had a headache since the day I left. When I got up the next morning after I came home from Chicago, I cooked my breakfast and sat down to eat it, but I couldn't. I just sat there and cried. I couldn't help myself. I tried not to think of you and to keep from crying, but the more I tried to hold it in, the worse I got. I never felt like that before. I just wanted to go off some-place and shoot myself. If I could I would come get you, but I have to get things done here for your arrival. I want to meet you in New York, if I can and I'm sure I can. I love you, take care of yourself. It's so lonesome here without you. God Bless you, I'll write again when I hear from you...

To read her dad's words of anguish was heart-wrenching for Barbara, but his closing was the biggest shock. Although she had always known he was a good man and took care of his family, he had never been religious. In fact, he was quite adamant about not going to church. Occasionally, Dorothy and Henry had a few words over that issue since she had grown up with a father who felt the same way. She had hoped that her husband would be different than her Da. Barbara remembered the only time Dorothy ever won the arguments was at Easter or Christmas and then only when she would beg him that it was "for the benefit of the girls". Henry knew he couldn't win that argument and begrudgingly went to church with his family. So Barbara wondered why he had said "God Bless you" in his letter.

Reading that first letter opened up a whole new view of the man Barbara loved so dearly and who loved Dorothy with his whole being, so she just had to read another.

My Dearest Sweetest Little Woman, I love you. I love you so much and believe me, when you get here, I'm sure going to prove it. You've always wanted me to say I'm crazy about you, and I am so crazy about you, I don't know what to do. I can't think since we been apart. I didn't want you to see how much it hurt me to go, but I tell you the world just stopped turning for me. I've felt so alone here and lonesome that I can't do anything. From the way things are, I don't believe I'll get to work on the house if I can't get in the mood. I'm afraid if I start on it, I'll bungle it. Darling, I need you, I know I sound like a teenager in love with his first girl, but I'm serious, I want you, life isn't the same without you. I'll never let you down, Honey, because you are all I have and the only one I care for, you know that don't you...

It seemed strange to read those words written by her dad so long ago; it was almost as if they were written by someone else. He was a wonderful father and family man, but Barbara certainly hadn't realized how passionate he could be. She knew he loved Dorothy with all his heart and would do anything for her, but Barbara never dreamed he could actually put it down on paper. And his writing "God Bless" was never really explained. Dorothy had always gone to church growing up so it would be no surprise to think of her praying, but Henry must have just had a moment when he needed a prayer, even though he would never have admitted it to anyone.

Barbara never doubted that her mom loved Henry just as much as he loved her, but reading her letters, Dorothy wasn't as verbal at the start. Her first letters were short and a bit impersonal in comparison. Even though she wrote that she missed him, her letters were more about her everyday life.

From Her:

Hello Dearest, everything seems so strange here, Honey, without you and I'm just lost. How are things going with you, Hon, are you eating in town or at your mam's? Let me know how you are doing. Mam and I are doing a big wash today so I'll finish for now to get this in the mail. I'll write again later, until then, Honey, I love you very much...

****

Hello Honey, I received your letter this morning and I was so pleased to hear from you. Things have been really hectic here and I have been so miserable I could have died. Honey, I miss you so much, but then I knew I would. I went to see about my entry permit into New York and I'll have to pick it up in London. Honey, when you send a package as you said, will you put in a can of Crisco? My brother, Jack, said he would give me some money to help out if you did. I'll close for now, but will write again soon. I'm always thinking of you and I love you so much. Your loving wife. Bye Bye.

Bye, Bye? That was certainly a strange way to close a love letter. But life hadn't changed that much for Dorothy at the time. She was still in England with her family, still working at her job and Henry was so far away in America, so she couldn't imagine how his life could be that different. But as time went on, she began to really miss him and her letters began to reflect it.

Hello my dearest darling. Your wonderful letter was such a comfort to me. Please keep them coming all the time. I think about you constantly, my sweet, and I miss you so terribly. Every night and every time I go upstairs I kiss your picture. It's our wedding picture, so I think of us at night. I'm sorry I've only sent short letters, honey, but I just feel dead on my feet and I've lost so much weight and my eyes are swelled up from lack of sleep. I must have looked terrible, because Mam's brother, Lawrence, came down and invited me to bathe there. It did feel so good to soak in the hot water. Then, my sister, Joyce, paid for me to have my hair set and it has improved my spirits. We went for a walk in the Abbey Park this afternoon and it was so beautiful and wonderful to feed the ducks. The flowers were such pretty colors. It did bring back many happy memories of the times we walked there. I love you with all my heart and always will. I need you too, Honey, and I know we will be together again soon. Don't worry, because I couldn't live without you either, my darling, so until next time...

My mom and dad, Barbara thought as she read letter after letter, it was so strange to think of them as young lovers walking hand-in-hand through the park, stopping to kiss or to sit on a bench watching the swans and feeding the ducks. Even though she had heard a lot of their fun stories of their courtship during her growing up years, she still was quite surprised to actually read their words of love and heartache that they, of course, had never shared with their daughters. Barbara realized she couldn't begin to imagine what it must have been like for them to be separated for so long so soon after their brief courtship and marriage. The distance between them and the months of separation must have seemed like an eternity. Barbara hadn't understood the importance of keeping the letters tucked away in that old wooden box, but after reading them, she began to realize how valuable they actually were. She certainly could at least now understand why Dorothy had kept all of his letters. What was most surprising though, was that Henry had kept hers! They were such an intricate part of their lives together. Barbara paused as she opened the next letter. She almost felt like she was intruding into their personal lives as she read page after page. She couldn't put them down. She could imagine her dad sitting at the kitchen table writing.

My dearest darling, I have just come from Fred & Di's and thought I would drop you another line or two. I got your letter yesterday and I feel a lot better. I've been eating in town two meals a day and I don't care for it. I fixed Di's washing machine for her and I believe it will be alright now. She thanked me with a good hot meal. I'm surprised it works since I feel like I can't do anything right without you. Momma and Papa are anxious for you to be here too. Momma has been having trouble with her knees again and she was bawling for all she was worth. She said she didn't know what she was crying about, she just wanted to cry. That's how I feel when I think of you. All I hear sometimes is the clock ticking and I just want to throw it away. You don't know, Sweetheart, how I feel to be without you. I'm just lost. I can't sleep nights and when I do go to sleep, I just roll and toss all night long and the next morning it looks like a herd of elephants ran over the bed. Honey, I know you are busy and tired and don't feel like writing, but Sweetie can't you write more than two pages? I can't live on just two pages. I want to know everything you are doing and how you are. I've just got to know or I'll blow my top. Tell everyone I said Hello and hope they are all well and to excuse me for not mentioning them earlier in my letters as I can only think of you. You are the only one I live for and God knows how I love and want you here. Dear, you are so good, you're the best little woman a man could have and I want you so much. With all my love, Henry.

Not only did he pour out his heart in every letter, he even got angry with her when she didn't write enough or write back to him as soon as he thought she should. He tried to keep it light and newsy about his life as he waited for her to arrive, but he always went back to how much he loved her and missed her.

As the months dragged on, Dorothy must have begun to feel the strain of her husband being so far away. It almost didn't seem like she had a husband until she got his letters.

Hello, my Honey, I received your letter this morning. I had my mail transferred to the shop so now I get a chance twice a day instead of once. I sent you some papers to write letters with. It's light weight paper like this, so you can write more than you do. After all, I wait a week to hear from you and all I get is three little old pages. I could get more on a post card than you do in all three pages. Don't you think I rate a little more? I have to hear from you or I will go nuts. I thought for sure that I would get your letter yesterday and when I didn't, I had the blues so darn bad I couldn't sleep wondering what was wrong. So please write more the next time. And what was the matter that you wrote the letter on the 16th and it wasn't post marked 'til the 19th. Surely it doesn't take you three days to walk to the post box.

I keep taking odd jobs to keep my mind at ease, but it doesn't help much. I did Dr. Small's blinds last Sunday and made $15.00. I then recovered some chairs for the Bennett lady for $5.00. I fixed Dr. Bell's lawnmower and he gave me a couple of dollars. I have a nice job coming up. I get to lay the linoleum in the Food Center. I hope to make pretty good pay from that job. My good friend, John Middle is going to help me.

We have had some pretty bad weather here. There have been predictions of a tornado coming, but I guess it went over us, although we had some awful winds. It did a little damage, tore down some TV aerials.

I got a pretty bad burn the day before yesterday on a drop light at the shop, but it's doing okay now. I could have used you here to help me get the bread out of the bread box as I couldn't lift my arms high enough. I need you more than you'll ever know. I just can't go on without you. I hope you get that entry permit soon. If you don't, you let me know and I'll do something from this side. So please go to London soon and get it. Don't wait, Honey, I don't want anything to happen to delay your arrival. I am glad everyone is being good to you there, but I could make you feel better here. Sweet God, how I could. I'll send a can of Crisco when I can.

Remember, my sweet, that the ink on the paper doesn't weigh anything, so you can write more than just the odd page or two. It is all I live for now to hear from you. I love you. You're all there is in this whole wide world for me. I can't even think unless you're on my mind and every day I have to talk to someone about you. John is a good friend, he's a good listener. He knows what it is to be away from his family too. I'll close for now, Sweetheart, 'til I hear from you again. Good night, Sweet. As ever, Henry.

Dorothy would write:

I waited for your letter all week, every time it was mail time, I kept going to the front door. Mam just laughed at me but today I was rewarded with a wonderful letter from you. How are you feeling now, sweetheart, are you more satisfied and resigned to being without us together? I knew it would be hard to be apart because we love each other so much, but we will have a lot of years together, honey, and they will be happy ones. I'm sorry, honey, that I haven't written enough, but I was so mixed up. This last week I had tonsillitis and was in bed for three days on doctor's orders. Your last letter made me feel better. I'll write more now because you come first, you know that. Mam and I went to the Brides Club last Thursday*and she introduced me all around to everyone there. I won a jam dish and got Mam a chance on a free trip to America. If she wins, she said she would come with me. Sweetheart, I send all my love, here's a big X which I'd give you if I was there.

I see you have been doing quite a few jobs to keep busy and save money. It's done nothing but rain for several days and it's been so miserable. I hope your Mam's knees are better. Do you want me to send some ointment? Well, my dearest, I wish I could hold you in my arms and hug you close. I do love you so much. I'm crazy about you, so until the next letter, please take care of yourself. Bye Bye, Fondest love, ...

In early 1946 the Transatlantic Brides & Parents Association (TBPA) was organized to assist the 45,000-50,000 British girls who left the shores of England to make a new home in the United States as brides of American servicemen. The organization's purpose was to keep the brides and their parents informed and in touch with each other when the war brides immigrated.

Barbara noticed that the letter ended with "Bye Bye" again, but she noticed too how Dorothy was starting to express more love and told him how much she missed him. The realization of the distance and time between them was truly becoming a reality. She had begun to make her letters longer as Henry had requested.

Chapter Two

Long before the letter writing started, the war had been raging in Europe since 1938, three years before Pearl Harbor was bombed and the United States entered the war. Dorothy Luann Parnell was born in Leicester, England on December 29, 1925 to Jack Parnell of Irish descent and Ellen Marie Wade Parnell. Dorothy was just a thirteen-year-old school girl at the beginning of the war. She attended Catherine Street Junior School, where she had started at age three.

When the war began in England, many of the children living in towns that were subject to heavy bombing raids became evacuees. They were evacuated to rural areas wherever possible and the urban schools closed. Teachers and children found alternative buildings such as village halls and warehouses for their classrooms. They would often assemble at some agreed point and then walk the country lanes to be housed in some suitable hall. The government realized this evacuation caused serious problems for education, so in November 1939, Prime Minister Neville Chamberlain announced that some schools in industrial cities would be reopened. Leicester was one of those industrial cities.

Even though Leicester had been relatively safe from bombings, the school children were still required to carry and sometimes wear their gas masks. "Oh, Mam, do I have to take that?" Dorothy whined about the gas mask she had to take with her every day to school. "It's so ugly and heavy too. Why do I need it?"

Understanding that it was difficult for a thirteen-year-old girl to grasp the meaning of the word "war", Ellen Parnell patiently explained about the gases that could be dropped with the bombs by the Germans or the Japanese.

It was hard for Dorothy to think of the Germans as bad. They had studied the European countries in school and Germany was almost a neighbor. To young Dorothy, the idea of them bombing England was difficult to understand.

"But, Mam, do I need to take it every day?" Dorothy whined. "Yes, of course you do, what would happen if they dropped a gas bomb when you were at school and you didn't have it?" Ellen told her daughter. Dorothy couldn't imagine it and didn't even want to think about it. Of course, everyone else at school had their masks too, so it didn't seem so bad to carry it, as long as she didn't have to wear that ugly, heavy thing!

"Oh, alright then, if I must." Dorothy sighed. Dorothy strapped the mask over her grey cardigan and stepped up on tip toes to kiss Mam goodbye. Ellen realized Dorothy was getting taller now and she didn't need to reach as far as she had before. Her little one was growing up too fast.

"Goodbye, me duck, you are my special girl and I wouldn't want anything to happen to you." Ellen said as she kissed Dorothy's head and watched her trudge towards the door. Ellen chuckled to herself as she watched Dorothy lugging the "hideous" thing down the street towards Catherine Street. But she felt comfortable that Dorothy would know what to do if the air raid sirens blared.

Ellen wiped her hands on her old plaid apron and turned to go back into the kitchen. She noticed a seam was coming loose on the apron and reminded herself to get out the mending kit after she had done the washing up of the breakfast dishes. She began to hum to herself as she started her days' chores.

Early gas masks were ugly and heavy. A family is shown sitting in their living room wearing them!

The Catherine Street school was only a few city blocks from home and a quick walk for Dorothy to get there. She hummed to herself as she skipped along the concrete street lining the endless rows of Council houses. She dragged her finger along the brick wall aimlessly. She was in no hurry to get to there, even though she thoroughly enjoyed school. She had recently performed in the school play as Little Lord Fauntleroy and had loved hearing the applause.

Ellen had been so proud, "Dorothy you were brilliant! Where did you get the courage? You didn't get that talent from me. I would have been terrified to get up in front of all those people. And, learning all those lines, how ever did you do it?"

"Oh, Mam," she exclaimed, "I could do it forever. I hope I can do more when I go on to Secondary School. Mrs. Beaker said they do many more plays with big parts and they invite the whole town to come to see it. Wouldn't that be grand! I shall practice very hard and maybe someday I'll become a cinema star. Wouldn't that be just lovely? I could buy you a new house with the money I earned." Dorothy indeed had big dreams. The carefree dreams of a young girl that would sadly come to an end.

Dorothy had sat for the exams for the next school level to go on, but Ellen didn't have the heart to tell her just then that even though Dorothy had scored well, there was no money for her to go on to the higher Levels. With six mouths to feed at home, the ration books didn't go far. Geoffrey and Allan, the only boys and the oldest of the Parnell children, were working and helped out some but had also married and had their own families to support. Dorothy's older sister, Joyce had finished school two years earlier, about the time little Victoria was born and as word of the war began. And then there was Paula in between them. With Dorothy, herself and Jack to feed, too, Ellen simply didn't want to tell her daughter at that moment just how scarce things were.

Chapter Three

Jack Parnell was a gruff man, strong-willed, with his Irish background. He liked his own pleasures. He gave just enough money each week to provide meagerly for the household needs and the current hungry mouths. He kept the lion's share for himself. It seemed as though Ellen had always been expecting a child and even now, near to being past the childbearing age, Ellen worried when she had to allow Jack his nightly pleasures. They couldn't afford another child.

"Ellen, where's my tea and porridge?" Jack bellowed from the living room table.

"It's coming," Ellen scurried to give the children a couple of scoops of the hot, thick porridge before Jack helped himself to the rest of the pot. She knew they needed something warm and nourishing in their stomachs before they left for the day. She watched disgustedly as Jack dropped bits of grape jam into his porridge before eating it. Ellen had never seen him eat it any other way. The added cost of grape jam made the pantry budget tighter, but she dared not get it. And even though the younger girls always cried for some, Ellen had to refuse so Jack would not be denied his morning grape porridge.

After finishing his bowl and gulping down his tea, putting on his worn blue work cardigan, having never owned nor driven a car, he would climb onto his bike and pedal off to work without a further thought to his family until the evening meal. They never spent much time together as a family. Ellen knew this was a blessing for her. The less she saw of him, the better she thought.

At the end of the day, Jack Parnell would come home tired and grumpy and no one would dare to interrupt him after his tea. His favorite spot was in the thread-bare green chair near the fireplace where he read **The Daily Mirror** for the rest of the evening. Ellen had wanted to replace that chair years ago before the war began, when they could have afforded it, but Jack would not allow it. Every evening, with the sun going down in the window behind him, his stomach full and a pipe full of tobacco, he would doze off and the family tried to stay quiet so as not to disturb him. The girls would read and Ellen would knit and pray he wouldn't burn the house down, so she watched him closely until the pipe's glow had died down.

Jack did put in a long day's work, so he was physically tired. He wasn't an old man, but his shoulders were slumped from bending over his gardens. His hands were rough and calloused from tending the soil with his spade and shovel. His face was free of hair but was weathered from the wind and sun. There were lines forming around his eyes from scrunching his face to keep the sweat and sun away. A smudge of dirt was across his forehead from wiping his brow throughout the day. He didn't joke or smile often at home, but when he did it changed his entire demeanor. He had a lot of friends who enjoyed his company at the local pub and he could be quite jolly if his numbers came up on the "pools" and would buy a round for the house. He always hoped he would have his "big come in", but the "pools" were just a teaser for him and he grumbled every night when he read the results in the **The Daily Mirror.** In any case, losing the money didn't stop him from spending it every evening on his way home. It was true, Jack Parnell was not particularly a family man regardless of the fact that he had fathered six children.

Chapter Four

The house where Dorothy lived with her parents and siblings was part of a row of Council houses rented from the government. The house was on Burfield Street, Leicester, England, the industrial town in the Midlands, north of London about ninety miles. The house always seemed crowded with the number of people living there. The three small rooms downstairs were the kitchen, living room, and front parlor. The fireplace was on the wall adjacent to the stairway door with a selection of various unmatched chairs positioned in front of it, as it was the only heat during the winter months.

Upstairs were two bedrooms across the stairwell from each other and a tiny back room that overlooked the garden and the outside toilet area. The small room was used for storage now, but had served as a little bedroom for the boys when they lived at home. They had shared the bed in the tiny back room, but took it with them when they moved to a rented flat closer to their jobs. Ellen had wanted to convert it to an indoor toilet facility but Jack had said it was not necessary so funds were not given. The stairway was enclosed and you entered from the door at the right corner of the main living room next to the fireplace. The heat from the fireplace did not reach the bedrooms upstairs so the beds were warmed with hot water bottles placed under the covers each night. Dorothy and her sisters kept warm snuggling in the one bed they shared. Jack and Ellen shared the room across the stairwell. The older girls were now old enough to hate the sound of the grunting and groaning coming from that room as Jack took his pleasure and Ellen did her wifely duty. If things got too loud, Joyce and Dorothy would quietly slip downstairs taking the younger girls to sit by the dying coals of the fire until they heard the sound of Jack's snoring.

To the right of the living room chairs was the dining table near the back window that looked out over the courtyard and the brick walls that separated their Council house from the neighbors'. The sideboard was on the wall opposite the fireplace where the dishes and utensils were stored. The walls were papered with a dull, dreary looking floral pattern that probably was quite fashionable in earlier days. Now it just looked old and dirty with the years of wear. Even if Jack would have allowed it, there was no money to replace it. Everything went to just keep the daily living expenses covered.

The narrow walkway past the sideboard went to the front parlor which was rarely used. In the winter, it was cold because it was too costly to stoke the fireplace in that room. In the summer it was hot and stuffy as the front window would not open to allow a breeze through the house. It was sparsely furnished, except for the old upright piano that Jack used to play in his younger days and a couple of old stuffed chairs. He had never learned to play the piano properly, but could beat out old tunes, such as **I Don't Know Why I Love You Like I Do (I Just Do)** on the black keys. In his younger days and happier times, the family sing along had been great fun. Those times were gone and now, the family's living space was the two main rooms downstairs and the small bedrooms up.

Council houses had begun around 1919 after WWI had ended and were a form of public housing built and operated by local councils to provide reasonable rents to primarily working-class people. Jack Parnell never earned enough to purchase his own home so the family made do with what they could afford. The long rows of brick houses were endless and every street looked exactly the same. The entire block was joined together as if one building, separated only by a long, dark, narrow, closed corridor/entry way to the back garden, a tiny piece of land mostly bricked in, but with a small spot for vegetable plants, a wire line for hanging clothes, and the toilet. Council houses in those days did not have indoor plumbing and the toilet was a single room attached to the back of the house. A water closet allowed the toilet to be flushed and drained into the sewers which were connected to the drain in the brick floor of the small courtyard where rainwater was also carried into the sewers. The back gardens were separated by five-foot brick walls and no one was ever allowed to climb those walls into the neighboring gardens. The ladies of the houses would talk over the walls with their neighbors and shared things about their homes and lives while respecting the other's privacy.

Chapter Five

Ellen Marie Wade Parnell kept their modest living space clean and tidy. She loved her children dearly and often wished she could give them more, but with Jack's meager offerings and the war rations, she had to make do with what was available. When she finally told Dorothy that she wouldn't be able to go on to the higher levels at school, they both cried.

"Oh, Mam, I know how hard it's been for you. I'll get a job to help out."

"You don't have to do that, luv. It's just that we can't afford to send you on to the higher levels. We will manage without you having to work. The boys help out when they can and Joyce is working now."

But Dorothy wanted to do her share to help the family, so at age fourteen Dorothy Luann Parnell left her beloved school and went to work, leaving her dreams of becoming a cinema star behind.

By the time she was nineteen, Dorothy had been working at the Wolsey for five years. During WWII, the Wolsey made men's underwear for the war effort. Wolsey, Ltd is one of the oldest recorded textile firms in Britain. It remains today as the largest hosiery company in the Leicester region, with goods exported worldwide. The huge brick building stood on Abbey Park Road across the road from the public Abbey Park, a favorite place for families to spend time during the summer months.

The River Soar runs through the grounds of Abbey Park, an area of fifty-seven acres. Its lovely gardens, ponds, walkways, and of course, the ruins of the 12th century Leicester Abbey were a quiet reprieve from the bustle of the surrounding city and the war. The park was the site of an annual flower show dating back to the 19th century, which evolved into the Abbey Park Show during the 1940s. The ruins of the old abbey contain a memorial to Cardinal Thomas Wolsey. The lovely park was quite a contrast from the looming stone building that housed the Wolsey factory.

Dorothy continued to live at home with her parents, older sister, Joyce and her two younger sisters while she worked. Her brothers, Geoffrey and Allan, married and started families of their own after moving to their rented flat. She and Joyce worked to help support the family since the war rations and limited funds continued to make daily living a struggle. Ellen had taken a part time job at a nearby clothes cleaner when Paula and Victoria went to school. Even then, making ends meet was difficult.

Inside the Wolsey it was cold and stark with exposed brick walls. The huge sewing floor room was dimly lit and the best light was on a sunny day. If you were one of the machine operators lucky enough to get a table near the window, it made for a good day at work. Not only the extra light to see, but the warmth of the sun helped keep the girls' hands warm as they sewed during the winter months. The floor became littered with scraps of material and thread throughout the day as the girls, most of them in their late teens or early twenties, sat at their huge double needle machines sewing garments for the British soldiers.

Dorothy had started at the Wolsey immediately upon leaving school. Some argue that the women were braver than the men who went to war. The men had weapons with which to fight back, the women didn't, they just had to take what was thrown at them and get on with it. A quote from a friend was, "Courage isn't doing brave things, it's doing what you think is right, even though you're scared. Don't think about being scared, remember the training, let the preparation kick in and just do it."

So, Dorothy tried to remember her friend's words as she became one of the young, healthy workers who were in great demand during the war effort. Her job title was what they called a "run-about", getting supplies for the sewing machine operators.

"Dorothy, can you bring me more thread. Dorothy, I need another bolt of cotton." The operators called out all day long for more supplies. The sewing room was large and there were rows upon rows of machine operators seated at the big tables. The distance from the fabric storeroom back to the sewing room seemed like miles as Dorothy ran from one end to the other of the sewing room getting the supplies the operators needed. When the floor got too littered with scraps, the run-abouts were to sweep their areas as well as get the supplies. It was hard work for a fourteen-year-old girl, as the calls continued all throughout the day, every day. Dorothy was exhausted when she got home each evening.

It wasn't far from her home on Burfield Street to the Wolsey, but Dorothy had no means of transportation, so she walked down Burfield Street to Brandon Street, then over to Belgrave Road. Even though it was a bit out of her way, when she had a little extra time, she walked past the entrance to the Cossington Recreation Grounds, known as "the Recky" to watch the boys and girls playing. A small red-headed girl was laughing and singing as she played on the swings. She reminded Dorothy of her friend Liza who had been her best friend at school. They had spent many hours playing at the Recky. Dorothy wondered where Liza was now and what she was doing. It seemed like an eternity since she had run and played with her friends. Catherine Street school was a long time in the past. She wished the war would be over and then maybe she could take some evening classes. She did miss going to school. She would even carry that hideous gas mask if she could just go back! Dorothy waved at the children playing, the little red-headed girl smiled and waved back as Dorothy turned and finished the last part of her walk to work. She headed down to Abbey Park Road and into the stuffy hot air of the Wolsey factory.

After a few months, saving a pence or two each pay day, Dorothy finally could afford to purchase an old second hand bicycle. Jack had seen it for sale on his way home from work and told Dorothy about it. It was rusty and beat up and could have used a coat of paint. The bell no longer worked and the basket was bent, but it was the most wonderful thing Dorothy had ever seen. The tires were good and Dorothy could ride to work in a matter of minutes, much better than walking the distance.

Ellen thought Jack should have purchased the bicycle for his daughter who had quit school to help out at home. When Ellen said so, Jack had laughed and said, "Bugger that, she's working now, she can buy her own bloody bike. I'm not made of money."

Of course, the bicycle meant even more to Dorothy, since she had paid for it with her very own savings and didn't need to ask her Da for it. Her life wasn't easy, but Dorothy found comfort in knowing that she was earning a small living for herself and helping her Mam. It didn't matter that Da was his usual selfish bear.

Dorothy worked hard at the Wolsey and when Dorothy was about seventeen, Mr. Garner, the floor supervisor, a short pudgy man who smelled of tobacco and alcohol, called her to his office. "Miss Parnell, come here." Dorothy was surprised, what had she done? She knew that the machine operators said Mr. Garner could be a particularly rough supervisor at times. Even though he had been relatively fair with her, Dorothy wasn't sure she liked him much either. He always smelled so bad and all the girls shared the same opinion. They quite often talked and laughed about him. Dorothy thought they were rude to do it where he might hear. After all, he wasn't really a difficult man, at least he hadn't been to Dorothy, so she tried to stay out of those conversations.

"Yes, Mr. Garner, I'm coming." Dorothy said as she propped her broom on the nearest wall and hurried to where he was standing in the doorway of his dingy office at the end of the large sewing room floor. It was across from the fabric storage room where he could survey the workers throughout the day. The machine operators had heard him call Dorothy out and they smugly whispered to each other, "Oooh, our Dorothy is in trouble. I wonder what she's done?"

As she approached him, Mr. Garner said, "Come in and sit down, Dorothy. I need to talk to you." Dorothy felt like a schoolgirl again being called to the Headmaster's office. She didn't know what she could have done wrong. She thought she answered the machine operator's calls quickly. She rarely made a mistake on which supplies they needed and she kept her area swept and tidy regularly. She suddenly had a thought that he might have heard the girls talking about him and assumed that Dorothy was in on the gossip. Oh, no, how can I explain that I never wanted to be part of their rude comments, she mused to herself.

Did one of the girls complain about me? She wondered, as she nervously took a seat in the small, crowded office that looked out over the sewing room floor. Well, I'll just explain as best I can and promise to do better, she thought to herself as she entered Mr. Garner's office.

At first glance, the office looked big, but she could see where papers were strewn all around the floor which made it seem cramped and much smaller. Mr. Garner's desktop looked like it hadn't been wiped off in years. Remnants of his lunch, a greasy paper of fish & chips, partially eaten, were on the corner of the desk. The ashtray was full of cigarette butts and, as usual, Mr. Garner smelled of stale tobacco and cheap alcohol, neither of which disguised his sweaty body odor. She couldn't help but wonder how he could get cigarettes and alcohol with the war rations in effect. Of course, he was the boss and one did not question the boss openly, no matter how strange the situation might seem.

His face looked unclean as usual, with the stubble of day-old whiskers. Dorothy thought to herself, 'Doesn't he ever bathe? I wonder if he is married. Ewwwe, what a horrid thought it would be to be married to him.' Dorothy quickly tried to put that particular image out of her mind.

The office was dimly lit, as the only window held a black drape to block out the light during evening air raids. She assumed that Mr. Garner must spend evenings working in his office if he needed a black drape for his window as there were none in the large sewing room or the fabric storage area to cover the windows there. That could explain his unkempt look if he spent evenings in his office. Perhaps he even slept there. Dorothy smiled to herself to think of Mrs. Garner tossing him out and him having to live in his office.

Dorothy shook off her thoughts and began to feel even more nervous as Mr. Garner walked around the desk to stand close by her. She could smell his breath and she felt the heat from his closeness. She wasn't sure what to expect as he continued, "Dorothy, you have been an excellent run-about for the past three years."

"Thank you, Sir," she managed to reply, as she looked towards the door in anticipation of making a fast escape. If he touched her, she would scream and run, she decided, even though she knew that would be the end of her job. Dorothy tried to remain calm and keep her voice from quavering. She didn't want him to know how scared and uncertain she was to be sitting in such close proximity.

Just when she felt she couldn't stand it any longer and she thought she would definitely bolt from the chair any moment and run to the door, his voice brought her back to reality and she heard him say, "Dorothy, I am promoting you to a double needle machine operator where you will sew the waist band on the men's underwear. There will be a shilling weekly increase in your wages."

In amazement, Dorothy choked out, "Oh, thank you, Mr. Garner, I promise I'll be the best operator in the building, you'll see." The pay increase was such a blessing! If his odor hadn't been so offensive, Dorothy might have given him a hug. Mr. Garner flashed a rare smile and Dorothy thought to herself, he should smile more often, it changed his entire face and she realized she had been right that he wasn't so bad after all. She left his office with a smile on her face, but told no one about her pay increase, just as Mr. Garner had instructed. Oh, if only those smug operators knew!

Over the next few months, many times she caught her fingers in the double needles as she learned her craft. The sewing machines weren't too difficult to run, but there was a required number of pieces to be finished each day and if that was not fulfilled, she had been told there could be serious consequences. Dorothy did not want to find out exactly what those consequences were, so she worked fast to get her quota completed each day. This meant the occasional catch of her fingers as the machine buzzed along the edge of the cotton briefs. Every machine operator had succumbed to the treacherous double needles and Dorothy was no exception. The machine would stop and the needles had to be carefully pulled out of the fingers and wiped clean. God forbid they should get blood on the material!

The operators looked out for each other and had welcomed Dorothy into their secluded club for she had been a good run-about and they appreciated that. When she caught her fingers, they would help apply some disinfectant and a bandage before they all went back to work. They all hoped the needles would not be broken, for if you broke the needles, it could mean the cost was deducted from your pay envelope. In a few years Dorothy became an excellent sewing machine operator and Mr. Garner rewarded her more than once with a few more pence in her weekly pay envelope.

Chapter Six

Some people don't believe in fate, but at the Wolsey, Dorothy was to meet a girl who would become and remain a close friend throughout the rest of her life and that certainly must be fate. Catherine Samuels was the same age as Dorothy and the first day they met at the Wolsey, they knew they would instantly be friends. They were both run-abouts and their designated areas were close to each other. Cath's warm smile and sweet voice made it impossible not to like her. When she saw Dorothy looking nervously around the floor of the sewing room, she had walked up to her. "Hello, my name is Catherine, are you new here?"

"Yes, it's my first day and I'm a bit scared. I've already heard that Mr. Garner is difficult to work for."

"Oh, pooh, he can be a bit of a bear at times, but he's alright. If you do your job and not complain, you'll be fine. Some of those cheeky girls moan about him too much. And they certainly should not have said anything about him on your first day. The machine operators can be quite rude at times. Don't you worry, luv, stick with me and I'll show you what to do."

Dorothy liked Cath's pretty smile and bouncy curly hair instantly. When Cath came to tell Dorothy it was lunch time, she asked her to come eat their lunch together and the lasting friendship began. After the girls had known each other for a few weeks, Cath shared about her family and how she was helping out with her pay. When Dorothy shared she was doing the same, their common ground brought them even closer together.

Cath lived a lot further from the Wolsey than Dorothy, but also walked to and from work. Bus fare was just too dear and Cath needed to save her money. Later when Dorothy showed Cath the used bicycle she had purchased, Cath asked Dorothy if she could help her get a used bike wherever Dorothy had found hers. Indeed, having a bike was a blessing. England, of course, is known for the regular rain showers that come when you least expect it. They don't usually last very long, but it can pour down quite quickly. Many times the girls would get drenched walking and bike riding to the Wolsey and home again.

"Oh, no, not again," Cath complained. It was the fourth time that week she had been caught in the rain. "I know," said Dorothy as they parked their bikes near the back loading dock. "It never lets up. I'm glad I got the bike though to get here quicker."

Cath agreed with a shake of her head and the water droplets splashed Dorothy in the face. "Bugger me, Cath, watch out!"

"Oh, sorry, luv. I've been thinking. Would you like to go shopping with me Saturday next? I've been saving a bit to get a new rain cape. I'd like a longer one to cover better."

"That's true. I could do with one as well. Saturday next, then, as long as Mam and the girls don't need me. I'll let you know on Friday."

When Friday came, they laughed and hugged each other when they ended up choosing the exact same rain capes. If they had had any doubt, they knew then they would always be friends. It seemed as though they were more like sisters. Many long hours would be spent talking about their lives and dreams for their futures.

Cath had been seeing a tall blond young man named Barney Kane for several months and the girls would often talk about their respective love lives or, in Dorothy's case, the lack thereof. Dorothy was a bit envious that Cath had a steady beau when she did not. There had, of course, been men vying for Dorothy's attention and she had accepted evenings out to the cinema occasionally, but no one had seemed quite right so there had never actually been any courtship. Cath had introduced Dorothy to her brother, Nevel and he and Dorothy had gone out together a couple of times also, but Dorothy just thought of Nevel as a friend and he soon found another gal who enjoyed his company more.

The girls often sat on the back loading dock at the Wolsey to eat their lunches, when the weather allowed. The spring of 1944 was unusually warm so they often enjoyed the chance to get out of the stuffy factory. The sun was shining and felt quite cozy for a change and they only needed a cardigan around their shoulders. Dorothy admired the one that Cath was wearing. It was a light blue and accented the blue of Cath's eyes. Dorothy felt her own brown eyes were not very exciting and even the pretty blue cardigan wouldn't have made her eyes sparkle like Cath's. "Cath, your cardigan is lovely, is it new? How ever did you afford it?" Dorothy asked.

Cath smiled a wistful smile that made her eyes shine even more. "It was a gift from Barney for my birthday. Isn't it simply delicious?" She smiled to herself as she gently ran her hand over the soft cable stitch on the sleeve of the cardigan and hugged it closer around her shoulders.

"Oh, Cath you are so lucky to have a man who buys such wonderful gifts." Dorothy exclaimed, with a bit of longing in her voice. To be lavished with such gifts was beyond her imagination. With the boys she had met, she was lucky to even get a cinema ticket, so a gift as beautiful as Cath's cardigan was only wishful thinking for Dorothy.

"Yes, me duck, I am most lucky. Barney isn't rich but he is very generous with his money. I told him that the cardigan was too dear and that he should take it back and get his money. But he just kissed me and said, 'Nothing is too dear for you, luv.' So what could I do, but keep it." Cath laughed as she shrugged her shoulders. Dorothy laughed with her and again secretly wished she had a steady fellow to give her new cardigans. Someday. She hadn't known on those afternoons on the loading dock of the Wolsey that her life was about to change forever in ways she could not even begin to imagine.

Cath and Dorothy's friendship was to last for many years to come, even across the ocean that eventually separated them. They wrote to each other still sharing tidbits about their families and lives until Dorothy passed away more than sixty years later.

Chapter Seven

Dorothy's workweek days consisted of sewing one waistband after another on the men's underwear at the Wolsey, but when she was nineteen, she got a job evenings and weekends selling tickets at a booth at the Leicester Speedway Racecourse, a dog track steeped in 100 years of history. The track featured tote betting, licensed bars, on-course bookmakers, off course betting windows, and a free car park. Hitting the dog races was always a top option for those who could afford it. They could fatten their wallet a bit before heading off to assorted nearby pubs for a drink or two or 'twenty'.

A sign at the track stated: **"Groups who are deemed too drunk on arrival will be refused entry"**. In spite of the occasional rowdy bunch, there was nothing like the thrill of a dog race to get your blood pumping and a possible opportunity to earn a bit of cash while your mates lost theirs. It was always a lure for those who liked to gloat!

"Hello, luv, gonna give me a winner tonight?" One of Dorothy's regular customers was at the window. "I hope so," she answered as she handed him the ticket. "Best of luck, to you," she smiled.

Quite often, Dorothy would receive a cash tip from a thankful winner who had purchased their winning ticket from her window. The extra money was a big help at home and she would thank them with her sweetest smile. Tonight was no exception. Her regular customer was back to cash his winning ticket. "You were indeed good luck for me tonight, Dorothy. Why don't we go out and celebrate?"

"Oh, thank you, but I've got an early day at work tomorrow." She graciously refused. It wasn't the first time she had offers of dates and always refused. She knew of her Da's penchant for gambling and didn't want any part of that in her life. "Well, then, luv, here's tuppence for sending me your luck, he smiled at her as he walked off. He staggered a bit and Dorothy knew he'd been drinking a bit too much. She reminded herself it was never a good idea to accept those dates no matter how much of a tip she got. She was pleased to get the tips, but remained cautious. When the track closed, she locked up her window after turning in the till for the night. She dreaded the long walk home, but it wasn't safe to ride her bike after dark.

Walking down the long streets lined with wall-to-wall Council houses was part of her regular routine and many evenings she had to feel her way along the walls of the streets to get home during the blackout. No streetlights were lit at night because of the war and all windows were covered with heavy black draperies to protect the city during the sporadic air raids. The bombers would fly over at night and any area where light shown would be subject to bombing. Consequently, everyone was very diligent in maintaining the blackout.

Fortunately, Dorothy knew well her way home, but the bricks were cold and dirty as she inched her way along in the dark to the opening of their entry way on Burfield Street. 'Why does there have to be a war?', she thought to herself. She missed the noise and the bustle of the streets as they had been before the war started, the children playing in the streets, shops open late in the evening, and the men and women with their shopping bags along the way.

Newton's Fish and Chip Shop on Catherine Street smelled good as she passed by. The remnants of fish and chips, fried in oil, still drifted out into the street, even though the shop had been closed for several hours and Mr. Newton was, no doubt, snuggled in bed with his chubby wife. It was obvious that over the years Mrs. Newton had eaten her fair share of rounds of fish and chips that gave her the robust figure that Mr. Newton so loved. Dorothy remembered all the times she had seen Mr. Newton pat his wife's behind as they worked together at the counter, dropping the batter coated fish into the hot oil.

As Dorothy passed the doorway, the odor reminded her of the days when she was young and would run into the shop asking Mr. Newton for a penny's worth of fish and chips. Mr. Newton always knew that Dorothy only wanted the chips and not the fish, but he would call out in his most important sounding voice, "A penith of fish and chips for Miss Parnell." Mrs. Newton would nod in understanding and grab a large piece of old newspaper and wrap up the mound of chips soaked in oil, vinegar and salt.

Mrs. Newton would hand the package to little Dorothy with a smile as she took the penny, "Enjoy 'em, luv," she called as Dorothy hurried out the shop door, tentatively taking the first chip out of its newspaper wrappings. The smell of the fishy oil and salt made her anxious to eat it and she often burned her young fingers on the hot chips for not waiting, but they were oh, so delicious!

As Dorothy made her way further along the wall, the smell of the fish and chip shop faded along with her memory of those days that seemed so long ago. She knew she wasn't far from home now just around the corner and a few doors down so she hurried her pace a bit. The night air was chilly and she pulled her cardigan around her tighter. The street was dark and quiet and the chill in the air made it seem a bit scary, even though Dorothy knew it was the same street she always walked down on her way home. She felt a sudden uneasiness that she hadn't felt before.

A noise behind her startled her and she stopped for a moment and listened. The streets were so dark you wouldn't see anyone until they were right upon you. Dorothy slipped into the closest entry way and waited. She didn't hear any footsteps and there was no further noise. She recognized the sound of a dog's feet clicking on the pavement echoing in the darkness as the dog approached. Dorothy had backed up into the open entry between the houses and hugged the side wall hoping the dog would not notice her. When he went along without a glance in her direction, she breathed a sigh of relief, just a stray dog that must have been trying to find his way home in the dark too.

She was glad it wasn't someone lurking in the shadows. Mam had warned her about men who could do some awful things to a young lady walking alone late at night. In spite of her relief that it was only a dog, she shuddered. Dogs were not Dorothy's favorite animal either. They had never had any pets when she was a small child, but she had been knocked down by a rambunctious neighborhood dog who, no doubt, only wanted to play, but that incident made her very leery of unknown dogs for the rest of her life.

Saying a prayer of 'thank you, Father,' that she had been saved from the dog or any potential attacker, she hurriedly walked the last few steps to her own entry way, silently slipped down it, and entered the back door into the kitchen.

The kitchen still held the lingering smell of the meager pot of beef stew that had been prepared for the family's evening meal. As she drew in the familiar odor, Dorothy instantly felt the hunger growl of her stomach. She had tried to ignore it all evening but now the smell of beef stew, after the smell of the fish and chips, made the empty feeling in the pit of her stomach all the more real. A quick look in the stew pot though, showed nothing available to ease that growing feeling of emptiness. Dorothy was just about to check for something else, when Mam came in.

Ellen Parnell had heard her daughter come in the back door and joined her in the kitchen, "Hello, luv, a long day? You want something to eat?" Ellen asked. "I can mash a pot of tea if you want."

"Oh, yes, Mam, that would be lovely," Dorothy said as she slumped down on one of the wooden chairs in the cold dingy kitchen. The only heat in the house was the living room fireplace and it didn't carry into the kitchen. The stone floor kept the kitchen colder, so it was helpful in preserving fresh food. There were no cupboards hanging on the walls, only the shelving that lined the walls where cans, boxes, and a few vegetables from Da's garden were stored. The kitchen was sparsely appointed, with only a small plain wooden table and two high-backed wooden chairs. The Parnell's Council house was indeed minimal, at best.

Dishes were stored in the sideboard in the main room. Family meals, which were rare, were taken in the main living room at the table there next to the window that looked out over the stone courtyard. Dorothy and her older siblings usually came and went so they just grabbed a meal when and wherever they could. It would have seemed strange to sit down together now and share their supper with Mam and Da and her sisters as they had done when she was little. The war had changed a lot of things.

Jack Parnell, of course, had arrived home long before Dorothy, and Ellen had fed him and the younger girls so they could go to bed with something warm in their stomachs. The beef stew hadn't gone far enough to allow a bit saved for Dorothy as much as Ellen tried. Once again, Jack Parnell had had his fill without a thought to any of the others.

Ellen hummed to herself as she put the tea kettle on the wood burning stove and stoked up the dying embers hoping it would be enough to at least heat the water if not the kitchen. "I'll make you some tea and toast. I'm afraid your Da has finished off the rest of the stew."

"Thank you, Mam, love you. The track was really busy tonight and I got a shilling tip from a lucky winner," Dorothy said as she handed the coin to her mother.

"Oh, Dorothy, love, this is your special money, I can't take it." Ellen protested.

"Yes, you can, Mam. I know the ration books are empty for this month and there's another week before you get the next book. It's not much, but it will buy a loaf or two at the grocer's." Ellen hugged her daughter and thanked her with pride and relief in her heart, as she knew that the dinner table would have a bit more for the next few days and she would be spared any guff from her husband. She was relieved that she would not have to hear his wrath if she asked him for more money. He could be even more disagreeable if he didn't get enough to eat, although he didn't feel the need to increase Ellen's weekly allowance regardless of how bare the pantry might be for the family, just as long as he got his fill.

Ellen left Dorothy to sip her tea while she took a slice of bread to the living room to toast over the open fire in the fireplace. Jack Parnell was snoring loudly in his chair and Ellen thought with some relief that she might not have to do her wifely duty that night if she didn't wake him. It didn't take long to finish toasting the bread and Ellen returned to the kitchen to give the freshly toasted slice to her daughter. There was a bit of meat drippings left and she spread it thinly over the bread and handed it to Dorothy. "Finish it all, luv, you need to keep up your strength." Ellen told her. Ellen worried about her daughter working such long days and then weekends and evenings as well. She knew Dorothy was young, but the war years had been taking their toll on everyone when there wasn't enough food to go around. She would have been even more disturbed if she had known that Dorothy hadn't eaten anything since her small cold chips and tomato sandwich at lunch time.

Dorothy smiled as she chided this wonderful woman who took such good care of her family in spite of the difficult times. "Mam, don't worry so much about me. I'm fine. This tea and toast will do the trick. Another one of the winners gave me some pence for chips." Dorothy lied to her mother. She didn't like to lie, but there was no point in worrying Mam any more than she had to about her empty stomach and besides, the tea and toast had helped. Dorothy liked the meat drippings on her toast better than butter anyway. The tea had been hot and Mam had put a bit extra sugar and milk in it even though Dorothy had told her not to.

After Dorothy finished her supper, Ellen cautioned her, "Be careful not to wake your Da when you go upstairs. You know how he is if he gets woke up suddenly." Dorothy hugged her mother and pressed her finger to her lips with a quiet, "Shhhh," and tiptoed into the living room. She passed her Da in his chair. He was snoring peacefully and most probably would spend the rest of the night there if the fire didn't burn out too soon and no one woke him. She vowed to herself that she would certainly not be the one to disturb him.

She was exhausted as she climbed the stairs to the tiny bedroom that she shared with her sisters. Four of them had to sleep in the same bed, but then it did keep them warm on a cold night. She was careful not to wake her two younger sisters. Joyce was still out with her beau, Ray. Dorothy had heard Mam softly creeping up the stairs shortly after her and Dorothy hoped Joyce would also be quiet when she came home to save Mam from Jack Parnell's wrath and lustful nature. He would be mad in the morning for having slept all night in the chair with no one waking him, but if he continued to sleep downstairs in his chair, then Mam could get some much-needed rest.

As Dorothy wearily slipped on her worn flannel nightgown she thought of Saturday evening next. The flannel nightgown was thin, but it would keep her warm enough when she climbed under the covers with her sisters. The thought of Saturday evening also gave her a warm happy feeling. She and Joyce were close in age and best friends. They were planning an evening out with Dorothy's friends, Cath and Nellie. Their plans were to go to the Corn Exchange dance just a few blocks from the street market in the main part of Leicester.

It was a long walk to the Leicester marketplace and the girls didn't want to risk having their bikes stolen, so they saved a bit of extra money from their pay envelopes each week to allow them to take the bus for their occasional night out at the dance hall. It was something they looked forward to and saving the money for the bus ride made it all the more special. The Corn Exchange was well known for bringing in different bands on Saturday nights throughout the month. Dorothy thought to herself, 'Regardless of who the band will be, I hope they will play my favorite **Glenn Miller, and Bing Crosby** tunes.'

She was looking forward to a long evening of dancing and laughter with her friends. It would be their own personal reprieve from the long days and nights working, but mostly from the war. Inside the dance hall, with the music playing and everyone smiling and having fun, one could forget, for a while, about the war raging throughout Europe and outside their doors.

It was getting late and now that she had a little nourishment in her stomach, Dorothy suddenly felt very tired. It would be another long day tomorrow so she'd best rest up to be refreshed for their Saturday evening at the dance. As Dorothy climbed into the crowded bed and snuggled next to her younger sisters, the warmth of their bodies next to hers made her drift off quickly to a peaceful sleep, dreaming she was dancing with a tall handsome stranger. She didn't realize that the coming evening out was going to be the start of an adventure for which she was not truly prepared.

Chapter Eight

Henry Donald Collins was born April 5, 1919, in a small town in Iowa. He was a twenty five-year old American serviceman, a Corporal with the 52nd Troop Army Air Wing as a Medic. The 52nd Troop Army Air Wing was established and activated on June 15, 1942 as an airlift Unit and flew aerial resupply and casualty evacuation flights of wounded service personnel. The wing was assigned to the Ninth Air Force in Sicily and moved to England in February 1944. During their tour of duty, reassignment was made to Amiens, France from March until June in 1945. The Troop operated until mid-June after V-E Day on May 8, 1945. They briefly returned to England, then back to France, before returning to the United States at the end of the war. While they were in England, they were stationed near Cottesmore, England at a Royal Air Force Station approximately thirty miles northeast of Leicester. It had permanent buildings and four C-Type hangars in 1942. In 1943, the United States Army had taken over the facility, flying troop transport aircraft from the base.

Henry's early story, although a continent away, was very similar to Dorothy's. His family was probably what the British might consider the American version of lower class. Although they were not in complete poverty, times were hard. The Great Depression began during the 1920s with the big stock market crash in 1929, affecting the entire country. Oklahoma and Kansas were devastated by what was to become known as the Dust Bowl. Prairie grass that grew in the area held the topsoil on the ground. But when the normal supply of moisture from the Gulf of Mexico was reduced, the prairie grass died and the topsoil was blown away. Some farms and farmers were in dire straits, which affected all local businesses and jobs. The southwestern part of Iowa was also affected by drought and loss of population due to the lack of jobs.

1932 was considered the worst year of the Depression, just about the time that Henry was thirteen years old and entering the eighth grade in school. Because of limited funds and large families, it wasn't unusual at that time for the young boys to leave school to go to work to help with the family's living expenses. Only about one fourth of them completed high school during those years. Henry was no exception and he left school after completing his eighth grade. He would have liked to go on, but he felt the need to leave school to go to work to help his family. His older brothers were married with families of their own and helped out when they could. Ren, his oldest half-sister also had her own family.

Ethel was just four years older than Henry and even though she had been seeing Jim Pearl, a family friend, she was still living at home with Momma and Papa Collins and Henry.

Since Henry was the youngest of her children, Bertha Collins didn't want her son to leave school to help the family. "Henry, I wish you didn't have to leave school and look for work. We can always manage," Bertha said to him when Henry told her of his decision.

"Well, Mom, you know you need the help, every little bit extra will make it easier. I don't need no more school as long as I can read and write and can use my hands. I have a strong back, I'll be okay."

"Yes, but there aren't many jobs around here. Lots of boys are leaving school and looking for jobs. What are you going to do?"

"I'll do any odd jobs I can find until there is better work. You know I'll do whatever I can." So for the next couple of years, he mowed grass, mended and painted fences, repaired bicycles and window blinds, anything to earn a bit of money.

One morning in early Spring of 1935 Henry told his mom, "I've heard that the railroad is hiring".

"Are you sure you can get a job at your age? It's hard work and I've heard they want older stronger men."

"Don't worry so much, Momma." So even though jobs were scarce, Henry, with his ability to smile and his sincere honesty, was fortunate enough to get employment with the C&NW Railroad, at sixteen. He had done a little fibbing about his age to get the job. It was only a slight blemish on his otherwise honest reputation. His momma hadn't been too happy about his lying to get the job but did admit that the extra money was a big help. In his young wisdom, Henry had known that the railroad was the best place to be.

Prior to railroading in Iowa, in the early 1800s, most travel and business shipping was done by river traffic. With the Mississippi River bordering Iowa on the East and the Missouri River on the West, Iowa was already an important economic center of the country because of the two rivers. Later, with completion of five railroads across Iowa, they brought more major economic changes to the state. During the late 19th century and into the 20th century, railroads provided year-round transportation for Iowa's farmers. With Chicago, Illinois' pre-eminence as a railroad center, the corn, wheat, beef, and pork raised by Iowa's farmers could be shipped through Chicago, to markets in the U.S. and worldwide. Prior to the Great Depression, Iowa towns also had six passenger trains a day. It can be said that railroads made industry and travel possible and connected Iowa with the rest of the world.

The railroads also created a significant demand for coal for the coal fired steam engines. The Southeastern part of Iowa, where Henry's hometown was located, became a vital area for coal mining and towns sprung up everywhere.

Henry was from a small town of approximately 3,800 today but in the 1940s it had a population of over 5,000. With the railroads and a boom in coal mining in the area, in the early 20th century, the region was dotted with the mining camps and company towns. Buxton, Bluff Creek, Lockman, Coalfield, Hocking and Haynes were some of the small coal mining towns in southern Iowa, none of which exist today.

Other than coal mining, the area's only claim to fame was that Rev. George Bennard had lived there. Rev. Bennard was a preacher and composer of hymns and wrote **The Old Rugged Cross**, in 1913. But in the 1940s most of the population could have cared less about Rev. Bennard and his hymns, because everyone was just this side of poor and having a composer as their only bit of fame didn't put much bread and butter on the table.

When Henry left school, he didn't know for sure what kind of job he would be able to get with his limited education. He had good manual skills, but the odd jobs were sparse and brought in only a little extra money. When he heard the Chicago and Northwest Railroad was hiring, he decided to apply, even though he was not very confident about getting a job. There had been a lot of boys from his eighth grade class who had left school with no intent to return. They, too, had looked for jobs with the railroad with no success. So after two years of struggling to get odd jobs, Henry decided he would try to get on with the railroad. He knew the C&NWRR had a satellite office in a nearby town, so he decided to take a chance and go there to apply. He really had nothing to lose and possibly everything to gain. "Put on your confident smile and let them know you are a hard worker," Henry remembered Momma Collins telling him.

The day that Henry headed to the C&NWRR offices, approximately twenty-one miles east of his home, he was nervous. He had just turned sixteen early in April and was still a slight built boy. Having no transportation, he started the long walk down the highway before the sun came up, hoping to hitch a ride. It was a chilly day and he huddled down in his jacket to keep warm. Not many cars were traveling the road that early in the morning and even though he had headed out before the sun had come up, Henry knew he couldn't walk the entire way in time to apply for a job; getting a lift was mandatory. A couple of cars had gone by without a second glance at the young boy trudging along the side of the road. The wind had picked up a bit and without any gloves on his hands and just a thin jacket, Henry knew the walk would be tough, but he was determined.

Henry heard the sound of a car coming behind him and he held out his thumb to signal the driver he needed a ride as the car approached. Without much confidence, he hoped the driver would take pity on him and stop. He stopped walking and put on his best smile. To his great surprise, the car slowed. "Where ya goin', kid?" the driver called out the window.

"I'm going to apply for a job at the railroad, sir." When the car stopped and pulled over, Henry ran to get in. "Thank you, sir. I was thinking I might have to walk all the way. I appreciate it. I don't have any money to pay you, but I could do some odd jobs for you. I'm good with my hands. I've been doing odd jobs around town and people say that I'm dependable and......"

"Whoa, slow down, you don't have to sell me, boy. I'm not lookin' to hire ya. I'm just goin' across the state to Illinois and I can drop you wherever you want along the way. Besides, it might be nice to have a bit of company to keep me awake. Ya say the railroad's hirin'?"

"Well, sir, I don't know for sure, but a buddy of mine said he had heard about it. I just got out of school a couple of years ago, and I've been helping my mom and dad doing odd jobs for people in town earning a bit here and there. But it would be great to get a regular job with the railroad and earn a little more money."

The two chatted back and forth and the time seemed to fly by. When they got to the edge of town where the railroad office was located, Henry was surprised that the journey was over so quickly. He thanked the man and got out, but as the car drove away he realized they hadn't even exchanged names. 'That's too bad,' Henry thought, 'I would have done some jobs for him.'

Henry had gotten out of the car on the west side of the industrial area of town where the roads were empty and no other traffic was around. As he walked closer to the C&NWRR building, it looked grim and foreboding from years of smoke from the steam engines coating the walls as they came through the station day after day. The wind was still blowing and it looked like a storm might be coming their way.

With a great deal of trepidation, Henry knew if he hadn't been so far from home and the fact that he needed a job, he might have turned around and headed back to the highway, but he knew his responsibility to his family. That's why he was there he told himself. So he pulled himself up to his full five-foot-nine and walked towards the building hoping he was showing more confidence than he felt.

The supervisor's office at the C&NWRR station was in a small dimly lit cubicle near the back of the station. As Henry entered, his first impression was that the supervisor didn't look very friendly. His desk was piled high with papers and he was leaning over them with a scowl on his leathery face. Henry thought he must have worked in the field for many years before getting a promotion to supervisor to be so weathered looking., 'Obviously, the promotion hasn't helped his disposition any,' Henry thought to himself as he cautiously approached the office door. Even though the door was open, Henry gingerly knocked on the outside door frame.

The surly looking man at the desk glanced up with a glare at being interrupted. "What do ya want, kid?" Henry cleared his throat a bit nervously, "I have heard that the C&NW is hiring, sir, and I would like to apply for a job."

The supervisor confirmed, "Yeh, we got a few jobs open for section crew workers, doing maintenance on the tracks. You don't look too strong though. We need good men to work the section crews. It's manual labor and hard work," the supervisor continued as he turned away to get more papers out of a beat-up old filing cabinet behind his desk. The clock on the wall was missing part of a hand, but it looked like it was around 6:00 A.M.

Henry cleared his throat and fought back his nerves so his voice wouldn't quaver. "I'm a hard worker, sir even though I don't look very big. I'm willing to take whatever you might have." Henry held his breath as the supervisor looked him over again with skepticism on his face.

"It can be long hours, but the pay is decent. Can you take orders and follow directions?" The supervisor asked gruffly.

"Yes, sir, I need the money to help my mom and dad. I'm the youngest and they are getting older and need me."

The supervisor didn't respond for a minute and Henry wondered if he was just being dismissed. He was going to turn and leave when the supervisor said, "Well, ok, then, I'll give you a chance, but only one. If you miss any work, you'll be done. I don't have time to coddle to no mansy, pansy kid who don't show up for work."

"I'll be here every day, sir." Henry promised and with a deep sigh the C&NW supervisor pointed out his soot covered window and said, "If you show up at the crew manager's shack out back at 5:30 A.M. tomorrow morning, you're hired. Now get out of here, I'm busy."

Henry breathed his own sigh of relief and with a quick "Thank you, sir," he left the building with a smile on his face. Maybe things would begin to look up for him and his family. Now, if I can just catch a ride home. Luck was with him, and he was saved from walking the twenty-one miles in the wind. That could have taken him all day. He was especially thankful since a cold rain had started to fall.

The next morning when his Momma called him, Henry was out of bed at 3:00 A.M. and headed down the road, hoping he would get a ride quickly and be at the crew manager's shack on time. He knew if he didn't show up by 5:30, there would be no job for him. He strode quickly along the edge of the road. The grass was just starting to turn green. It had been a long winter and spring was late. The crunch of the gravel beneath his feet kept a steady rhythm as he walked along. A few early birds were singing in the trees along the road with the promise of better weather to come.

It was so early, there were no cars traveling the highway at that time of the morning. Henry's legs were young and strong and he began sprinting partially to get there faster, but mostly to keep warm. The sun wasn't quite up that early and the dew on the grass from yesterday's rain made the chill in the air cut through his body. Henry pulled his jacket collar closer around his neck and shoved his hands in his pockets. 'I'm going to get me a pair of gloves with my first pay', he thought to himself.

After trudging along for over an hour, Henry was getting worried that he wouldn't make it to the crew manager's office on time if he didn't get a ride. He couldn't walk that far even if he did have strong legs. He wasn't sure how far he had to go yet, but he was feeling discouraged. If he didn't get there on time, there was no hope for a job. His family was depending on him so he had to get there. He stepped up his pace and tucked his head down further in his jacket to keep the wind out of his face. When he heard the car coming behind him, he immediately stopped and put out his thumb, hoping the driver would be kind enough to stop. To his surprise, the car stopped right away and a smiling young man said, "You're out hitching a ride awfully early. Hop in."

"Yes, sir, I was hoping to get a ride. Thank you, I'm Henry Collins and I'm going to the C&NWRR for a job this morning. I have to be there by 5:30 A.M. or there's no chance of getting it." Henry spilled it all out without a breath in between. He had been quick to introduce himself as he climbed into the car. He didn't want to make the same mistake as the day before. "What's your name, sir?" Not everyone wanted to stop for an unknown hitchhiker, so he wanted to make sure he learned who had been so kind so he could repay him in some way.

John Middle was a muscular young man who was only about three or four years older than Henry. But, he had a slightly receding hair line that made him seem a bit older. He had a generous smile and introduced himself, "John Middle, boy you must want the job badly to be out here so early."

"I didn't know if I would be able to get a ride, so I started out early in case I had to walk all the way. This job is very important to me and my family." Henry replied.

John Middle laughed a big belly laugh that seemed to come from his toes as he thought of the skinny kid walking twenty-one miles and said, "Well, this is your lucky day. You won't have to spend your day walking, I work at the C&NW crew office and I'll be going there every day too. If you get the job, we can share the ride if you like." Henry couldn't believe his good luck. He smiled his thanks to John and hoped they would become friends. He told John if he ever needed any handy man jobs, just to let him know. The agreement was made with a handshake when John parked the car.

Henry headed to the crew shack and was pleased that the promised job was waiting for him. But he soon discovered just how hard the job was going to be. That first day was even more physically demanding than Henry had thought; he caught on fast though to the instructions and the line supervisor decided he might become a decent maintenance crew worker if he continued to learn so quickly. Henry soon found that the days were long and busy. There was no time for slacking. In good weather the maintenance crew worked outside replacing track and worn couplings on the cars and Henry enjoyed it. Part of the time, their jobs included spreading an asbestos mixture on the boilers of the steam locomotive to prevent fires aboard the engines. (Being around the asbestos may explain in part why Henry was diagnosed with cancer in his late fifties.)

Working on the maintenance crew was indeed a tough job as they worked in all kinds of weather. The jobs had to be done no matter what, but most of the guys wanted to be on the track's maintenance crew during the summer months and then do the asbestos spreading to the boilers during the winter so they could be inside where it was warm. The other way around was miserable.

There was a lot of "brown nosing" to get the best assignment, but everyone also knew you worked where and when you were needed. Henry just wanted to put in his day and get his pay so he did whatever he was told without complaining like some of the guys. The summers outside were not so bad unless there was a long hot spell. With the sun beating down on his neck and the sweat running down his back, it wasn't unusual for him to come home with a sun burn at the end of the day.

"Oh, no, not again, Henry. Why do you take off your shirt?" Momma Collins said when she saw Henry walking up their sidewalk. He was glowing bright red.

"It gets hot out there, Momma, a bit of a sunburn doesn't matter. I can get just as burned on the steam boiler if I'm working inside, so what can I do? If it was cold outside, I'd be getting frostbite. It's all part of the job." Momma Collins pulled a bit of cold lard out of the icebox and smoothed it along his back. She knew that would mean a little less lard for cooking, but she didn't want his back to blister either. Henry felt the coolness of the lard take some of the sting out of the sunburn and he closed his eyes and drifted off to sleep on the couch. Momma Collins whistled softly to herself as she prepared supper for him and Ethel and Papa.

Even though it was a hard job working for the C&NWRR, the pay was decent and regular as had been promised. The physical labor kept Henry slim and he grew stronger as time went on. His young body developed some good muscles. He also made some good friends at work, especially John Middle, who had so generously given him a ride that first morning and for the ensuing time afterwards. Henry would never forget that act of kindness and many years later he was able to return the favor by hiring John as his assistant at the factory where Henry had taken the position of Maintenance Supervisor. Their roles reversed, but their friendship remained intact.

Chapter Nine

When the war broke out in Europe in 1938, Henry was just nineteen and still working on the railroad. Then, when the Japanese bombed Pearl Harbor in December 1941, President Roosevelt announced that America was entering the war. There was lots of talk in southern Iowa amongst the young men about joining the service. Even though the war had been raging in full force in Europe for quite some time, the young men were caught up in the enthusiasm, excitement, and glamour of going "off to war". Henry decided to sign up, along with a lot of the other young men from the surrounding area, much to the chagrin of Momma Collins.

Since Henry's older brothers and sisters were married with their own families when America entered the war, his brothers did not enlist. As an unattached male, Henry felt the urge to go to help defend his country. When Randall, Henry's nephew, son of his oldest sister, heard Henry was enlisting, he decided to join too. Randall was five years younger than Henry and still acted very immature at times. Henry wondered if Randall would be sorry he decided to join the military service. Henry was sure Randall could not imagine the consequences of that decision. At seventeen, he just loved the sound of being a soldier in uniform and, of course, wanted to do whatever Henry was doing. Randall's mother, Ren, was not happy that he was going to tag along with Henry. But Randall couldn't be convinced to stay at home, so Ren made Henry promise to watch out for Randall.

Momma Collins was not happy to have her youngest son, her baby, join the service either. She secretly prayed, Lord, if Henry must go, can he stay stateside? I don't want him to go into battle and be killed. I couldn't bear it. She feared what could happen. So many men were needed overseas and it made her worry that Henry might be in danger if he was assigned to the front lines. She made him promise to write home during his basic training and inform her of his assignment for his tour of duty. She was even more worried when he wrote about how he was learning to handle an Army rifle and how to break it down and clean it properly. She feared that meant he was being trained for the infantry.

Henry had no problem learning to handle his rifle since he and Papa Collins had hunted when he was growing up at home. James Peter Collins had taught all his boys to live off the land. Fishing and mushroom hunting was a must to supplement the family meals. He taught them how to hunt animals safely and to skin their kill. Deer, squirrel and rabbit were staples on the Collins' dinner table. But even though Henry had killed animals for food, Momma Collins wasn't sure how her gentle kind-hearted boy would handle having to shoot another human being.

"Henry, I know you feel you have to go," she said to him as he was packing his clothes. "But, I think there are probably enough boys going from here already. You know we need you to help out with the family."

"Momma, don't worry, I will be fine and I'll send as much of my pay as I can. It should be even more than what I earned at the railroad, because I won't need much with everything that's provided by the Army. I will be alright, you'll see."

Momma Collins knew that they could manage without the extra money, she had managed before and could do it again. But it was part of her futile efforts to convince him to stay. Her words fell on deaf ears, of course. She continued to hope she could get him to change his mind about enlisting. Even at the late date, as she watched him pack his few belongings, she felt compelled to try again. She also knew that when Henry made up his mind, there was no changing him. So as she watched him finish packing, she decided to keep her worries to herself and instead said, "Please be careful, my boy. I don't know what I would do if anything happened to you," she said as she turned her head to wipe away the tears from her eyes, hoping Henry wouldn't see.

Those were tears Henry had rarely seen from this strong woman who had raised five children. She had cooked and cleaned every day without complaint. He didn't even remember her shedding tears when she lost the babies she had when he was younger. Probably she was relieved that she didn't have more mouths to feed and bodies to clothe. Life had been tough enough without more children. So, in spite of his mother's worries, pleading and tears, Henry left home to defend his country, with young Randall tagging along.

Henry's oldest brother, Charles, picked the boys up and took them to the enlistment office in the capital city. "I can't believe we are actually going," Randall chatted endlessly in the car. It was only a fifty-five-mile drive there, but to Henry it seemed more like a hundred fifty-five as Randall continued, "Where do you suppose we will go first? Will we get training first or will they give us a gun and send us off to kill Nazis and Japs right away? I heard they needed soldiers on the front line right now. I can hardly wait to kill me some Japs and Nazis."

As Henry listened to Randall chatter in his excitement, he secretly hoped he would get an assignment somewhere away from the front line and Randall. Listening to him chatter for a full three-year tour of duty would not be fun. Henry tried to tune out Randall as the road took them farther and farther away from home. The fields were fully planted and the corn was already higher than knee high and it wasn't even the 4th of July yet. He watched the straight rows of green stalks steadily go by taking him to a new, unknown adventure. He already was a bit homesick, but he also wasn't afraid to go to the front line or to die for his country. It was just that he couldn't imagine actually having to kill someone. "Well, I suppose if it's them or me," Henry thought with as much confidence as he could muster. He looked out the car window watching the tall corn stalks swaying in the wind. He knew it would be a long time before he would see them again.

When they finally arrived at the enlistment office, Henry was weary from Randall's endless chattering. As they gathered their belongings and headed to the enlistment office door, Charles shook the hand of his youngest brother and said, "Now you take care of yourself kid. Ma don't want no telegram about you getting shot or killed." That thought hadn't yet occurred to Henry. He couldn't imagine how Momma would react. But the realization rushed in quickly and Henry threw his arms around his big brother for a quick hug. He made his voice sound as light and positive as possible and said, "Don't worry, I'll be careful, besides Randall's going to kill all those Nazis and Japs for me!"

We don't know if Randall did in fact kill his share of the enemy, because sadly, he failed to return from the war. He had attained the rank of Sergeant with Company 1, 333rd Infantry, 84th Division and was killed in action on November 22, 1944, at the age of twenty. The family was devastated at their loss. Sweet, kind Randall who hadn't even wanted to go hunting with his dad and brothers when he was young, took to his duties in the infantry with relish and died a hero. Henry's grief tore at his heart even more when his sister, Ren, wouldn't forgive him for breaking his promise to look out for Randall. She blamed Henry for losing her son and took her grief out on him and his family.

Chapter Ten

Basic Training went by quickly and Henry's Unit had gotten their assignment to Europe. Momma Collins was upset that he hadn't been assigned Stateside. Henry didn't know what to expect going overseas, but he was anxious to see how he would do as a Medic. He knew he had done well in the training, but was sure things would be very different once he was on active duty. He vowed to do his tour well and return home to Iowa.

Henry had been a bit nervous when he learned that his Unit was getting ready to ship out. He'd never been far from Iowa before and Randall had been assigned to another Unit, so he would now be alone. 'Boarding a troop ship to cross the Atlantic Ocean is going to be a whole new experience,' he thought with some trepidation.

The crossing had taken a little over two weeks and had proven to be a bit rough when the big, lumbering troop ship rocked back and forth with the waves. Several of the boys succumbed to motion sickness and were glad to get off that constantly swaying monstrosity. Henry managed to keep his food down and was only plagued by daily headaches. Working on the moving trains during his younger days with the C&NWRR he had developed a resistance to motion sickness. As he stood on deck taking in the fresh air, he thought to himself that he was relieved that Randall's Unit was going to France on a different troop ship. His constant chattering wouldn't have helped Henry's headaches during the long crossing. But he did miss Randall. In spite of his tendency to non-stop communicate his every thought, he would have been a comforting contact with home. Henry didn't realize he would be so homesick. 'Men don't get homesick', he told himself. 'Shake yourself out of it, Henry.'

Henry spent part of his time each day reviewing what he had learned in Basic Training so he would be ready when he arrived at the new base, but he also had a lot of free time to wander around aboard ship after his turn at KP duty.

As he stood at the railing watching the endless sea rolling, Momma Collins' face was always in his mind. Henry remembered some of the tunes she would whistle as she worked and he began to whistle them as he leaned over the rail of the troop ship looking for the site of land. "I've been working on the railroad, all the live long day......" Henry laughed to himself as he thought of that old song. The whistling brought back special memories of home and his days on the railroad. He soon forgot his current headache as he thought of Momma Collins hanging freshly washed clothes on the rope line that ran down the length of their back yard. The summer breezes would dry the clothes 'til they were stiff and crisp, but with the smell of the fresh, clean, outside air.

He remembered the long happy days of summer when they would run and play without a care in the world. Henry missed the days of hunting with his dad and the closeness they had shared after his older brothers had married.

Henry thought about the day that Papa Collins had found an old rusty bike at the town dump site. He loved going to the city dump and often brought back more than he took! The bike was in bad shape, but Papa Collins assured Henry that if he was diligent, he could restore it enough to make it serviceable enough to get him around town. Henry remembered after several weeks of working on it, the bike had gotten him to school, to places with his buddies, and later to his part time jobs. It even provided good experience at restoring old items, which helped bring in additional handy man odd jobs when money was tight. Unfortunately, the bike was long gone by the time he began his work on the railroad. Henry thought how it would have been nice to have it on that first cold morning when he had been hitch hiking to get to the job with the railroad. A neighbor had backed over it in the street and bent the frame beyond repair. There had been no money to buy another. Momma Collins had chastised him for leaving it so close to the edge of the road. It was a lesson well learned.

Henry was so absorbed in reminiscing that he didn't notice the sound of footsteps coming across the deck of the troop ship. He was suddenly pulled out of his daydream and brought back to the reality of the huge ship crossing the immense expanse of water, when a familiar voice behind him said, "I thought I'd find you here."

"Oh, Hi, Joe. Yeh, I like the fresh air better than being cooped up in the cabin, so whenever we have some free time, I come up here. It kind of reminds me of home, you know, the peacefulness. When I was a kid, Papa would take us boys down to the creek to fish and it was always so quiet and peaceful. We would sometimes sit there for hours with only the sound of the birds and the trickle of the creek. Only our whoop and holler when we caught a big crappie would break the silence. It sure seems like a long time ago now."

Joe smiled, "We didn't go fishing much, there was always so much to do in the fields, but I do think about the nights after the work was done and Mammy would have supper ready and we would sit out on the porch to eat it when it was too hot inside. The sound of the cicadas singing would fill the night air."

The two of them stood quietly on the deck, each reflecting on how their lives had been just a few months ago and how they were now changing faster than they could have imagined.

Henry had met this young man from North Carolina during Basic. His name was Joe Foster, who was their Unit's driver. Joe had a delightful smile that lit up his face when he laughed. In addition to that smile, was a crop of brilliant red hair. It made him stand out in any line. Joe was taller than Henry, well over six feet. Consequently, he was a little self-conscious of his height and was prone to slumping a little at the shoulders. This gave him constant reprimands from his C.O., "Stand up straight, Private". Joe tried hard, but always seemed to be an irritation to the commander no matter what he did. His southern accent charmed most everyone except the commander. Everyone agreed that Joe was sometimes hard to understand but they enjoyed listening to him talk. That infuriated the commander and seeing the friendship developing between a young white Medic and the Unit's black driver infuriated him even more. It could reflect badly on his status as Commander if it got back to the higher ups that he was allowing fraternizing between the blacks and whites. He vowed to watch Joe carefully and report any improper behavior.

Henry particularly enjoyed listening to Joe talk about his life in North Carolina where he and his family were tobacco farm workers. Henry smoked **Camel** cigarettes, but he had never seen tobacco growing and didn't know anything about the process, so hearing Joe's stories was interesting and helped pass the time.

During one of their long evenings aboard ship after their duties were done for the day, the boys sat and talked and Joe had said, "Yep, my family has been tobacco farm workers for a long time. North Carolina has a long history of tobacco growing that has spanned almost three centuries. Did you know Sir Walter Raleigh was the first explorer to bring the leaf to Europe, and in later decades before the American Revolution, settlers in Carolina grew tobacco with moderate success along the Atlantic coastline?" Henry didn't really know for sure what Joe was talking about, but Joe loved to talk about tobacco farming history and it made home seem a bit closer for them both, so Henry had let him ramble on, even though it sometimes made Henry a bit more homesick.

Joe continued, "In the 1880s, a new tobacco boom occurred in the state when Washington Duke introduced mass-production techniques in cigarette manufacturing. From then on, tobacco growing and manufacturing has been the largest source of income for North Carolina. On average, it takes 900 man-hours of work to <u>cultivate</u> one acre of tobacco 'cause we do it all by hand. No machinery for the cultivating, just hard labor." Joe continued as Henry listened with genuine interest. He would think about what Joe had told him the next time he lit up a **Camel**.

"Whoa, I can't believe it." Henry had replied in amazement. "You do work hard. I can see why you've grown so tall." The boys laughed with each other at the new friendship that had developed between them. Quite often they were assigned to the same duty roster when Joe wasn't driving. They had soon become friends and were delighted to learn that they were shipping out to England in the same Unit.

Henry felt the long ocean crossing was bearable with Joe's friendship and he was thankful to have met him. The boys were about the same age and Joe had come from a large family too. He had three brothers and three sisters and he too was the youngest in his family, the same as Henry. His family had a long history of working on tobacco farms. Joe said he had been told that some of his ancestors had been slaves. The boys had often laughed over Joe's red hair when Joe said his family tree must have included a white, red headed slave boss somewhere along the way. It wasn't something Joe talked about very often, but Henry had also shared with Joe that his family had an American Indian history. Papa Collins's first wife was full Cherokee. She had died young, after giving birth to Ren, Henry's oldest half-sister. Papa Collins then married Clare Bertha Thomas and had the rest of the Collins children, so even though there was no Indian blood in Henry, that ethnic tidbit brought the boys' friendship closer. They realized that even though they were from different backgrounds and their states were far away from each other, they were a lot alike in many ways regardless of the color of their skin.

The only time they verbally acknowledged they were a bit homesick was to each other. It wouldn't be wise to admit it in public company for all to hear. The C.O. and the other guys would have given them a hard time about it. Joe's Mammy wrote to Joe regularly just like Momma Collins did and the boys would share their letters from home. They both wrote home about their friendship, and their respective mothers came to feel like they knew the other boy as well as their own. One morning while they were standing on deck, Joe said, "Henry, I got a letter from Mammy just before we shipped out. I didn't share it at the time, it was bad news".

"You want to talk about it now?" Henry asked his friend. "You don't have to if you don't feel like it, but I'm ready to listen if you want."

Henry waited as his friend took a deep breath and continued, "Yeh, Mammy said my oldest sister, Caroline, had her baby earlier than expected and it was stillborn. She said the family was devastated since it had been her first baby and they had been so excited when they had learned the news of a baby on the way. The doctor had told her it might be a complicated pregnancy since she was in her late thirties, but she and Brett were so thrilled, they didn't even want to think about any problems. They have been married for twelve years and had given up on having children, so it's been quite a shock and everyone is having a difficult time." Anger began to rise in his voice.

"I wish I was there; I should be there!" Joe's voice became louder and echoed the pain he was feeling. "They need me at home now, not crossing this stupid, huge, ocean, going to God knows where."

Henry's eyes welled with tears as Joe shared the heartbreaking news from his mom. Henry placed his hand on Joe's back, "Joe, they know that you want to be there, but they also know that what you are doing is important too. You're protecting them and our country and that means a lot to them, I'm sure."

Joe wiped away his tears on his sleeve and nodded his head. "Thanks, Henry, you're a good friend and I'm sorry I didn't share it with you sooner. I just didn't know how to tell you. I didn't want to make you feel bad about leaving your family. I know they are probably going through tough times, too. My sister is a strong healthy gal and I hope she and Brett will have other kids."

Henry chuckled and replied, "She'll probably have a whole slew of babies before we get home!" The boys laughed together, and Joe thanked Henry again for being such a good friend and how he felt he could get through this war because of their friendship. Having Joe's friendship meant a lot to Henry, too. Months later, when Momma's letter had come telling him about Randall being killed, Henry had told Joe. Joe sat with Henry and let him spill out all his feelings of sadness. Their friendship bonded through their grief.

Chapter Eleven

Basic Training had gone well. Combat medics (also known as just medics) were military personnel who had been trained to at least an EMT-Basic level (normally a sixteen-week course in the U.S. Army) and who were responsible for providing first aid and frontline trauma care on the battlefield. They were also responsible for providing continuing medical care in the absence of a readily available physician, including care for disease and battle injury. Combat medics were normally co-located with the combat troops they serve in order to easily move with the troops and monitor ongoing health. Henry was looking forward to putting his training to good use as the days and nights aboard ship seemed to endlessly drag on. He was particularly glad Joe had been assigned to be the Unit's driver.

When land was finally sited, the men were extremely glad to get off the ship as it docked. But the feeling of solid ground beneath their feet was short lived as they were immediately loaded onto troop trains to be transferred to their post assignments. Joe and Henry were headed for their first base assignment in Sicily. They were both glad to be off the ship and Henry enjoyed being a passenger on a train for a change, instead of the railroad crew. Joe had never been on a train before and was a bit apprehensive.

"Oh, this might be worse than the ship." Joe said as the train pulled out of the station and began to sway along the tracks.

"You'll be okay once you get used to it, just like on the ship. Just focus on the scenery, it's a whole lot better than the ocean." Henry told his friend and Joe agreed. They watched the villages and fields go by and it reminded them both of home. The countryside was quite different from Iowa and North Carolina, but just the houses and green fields made them both a bit more homesick. Cattle and sheep were scattered along the hillsides and the boys closed their eyes and thought of home.

The train ride seemed almost as endless as crossing the Atlantic. It slowed as it came through each little town and village, although they never stopped. They saw passengers patiently waiting on the platform for their trains and some of them waved at the young American soldiers hanging out the open windows. The locals were glad to have America join in the war effort. Now they would take down those Germans and Japanese!

When they finally arrived, Henry and Joe found that their days on the base were busy as soldier after soldier came in, were treated, and either went back to their Unit or were shipped home to recuperate. Henry became quite close to some of the injured men who had spent several months being treated and recuperating at the base before they were shipped back to the States. When it came time for the injured to be shipped home, Henry was sad that he couldn't go with them. But that feeling didn't last long as there was always more injured coming in.

In February of 1944, Henry and Joe's Unit was transferred to Cottesmore, England. Henry enjoyed being a medic and was glad of the assignment, not only that it kept him from fighting at the front line, but also because he loved being able to help his injured buddies. As a medic, Henry had to learn how to clean and bandage a wound. How to put on a simple tourniquet and to give a hypodermic shot was part of the basic things a medic needed to know. Henry didn't realize at the time that he would learn a lot more things once he was on active duty. When the men would be brought in from the front lines, many of them were wounded far beyond the training Henry had been given, but he soon learned how to start a good IV line and to do whatever was needed to help the injured.

Some of the men had lost limbs or were blinded by explosions. Many of them were recovering from surgery to remove shrapnel. Henry felt such sympathy for them. He would often spend his free time sitting with some of the men and read them their letters from home. If a soldier wanted to write back, Henry would sit and write it down as the boy dictated.

"Thank you, Henry. It's good of you to help me," said one young man who had lost his right arm.

"Hey, it's fun to hear about your family. It does help with the homesickness to learn things about them," Henry had told many of the wounded. "When I hear your news, it's like I'm getting an extra letter from home." As he sat and talked with the wounded boys and read to them, he had often wondered where Randall was stationed and hoped he would be alright. So, when the letter came from Momma Collins, it was a painful shock, one that Henry carried with him for the rest of his tour of duty. He felt responsible for allowing Randall to go with him to enlist, although in reality, Randall would have gone anyway. He felt blessed to have been given the medic assignment when Randall was with the infantry. Randall had wanted that assignment so he could kill lots of Nazis and Japs. But it made Henry feel like maybe he wasn't really doing his own part in the war effort to the fullest.

Chapter Twelve

As the weeks and months dragged on, the boys looked forward to passes from the base Commanding Officer. An evening away from base was a much desired and needed reprieve for all of them. Joe would drive the camp truck that would take them and bring them back again. Leicester was about thirty miles away from the small village at Cottesmore where there was not much to do. The RAF base wasn't large and didn't offer much in the way of diversion from duties. There was one small pub on the main road of the village, the **Cottesmore Red Lion**, that was always full of soldiers, both Americans and British, but if the boys wanted more "action" they needed to catch the camp truck into Leicester.

That meant you had to get a special pass from the C.O. to leave the area. He was usually pretty good at passes for the local village, but giving passes to go into Leicester was another thing. You had to really do your job and not cause any problems. Henry was rewarded with regular passes, but some of the guys who didn't like authority didn't do as well. Their jealousy made them often complain that Henry brown-nosed the C.O. They couldn't appreciate the extra work that Henry put in to get those passes.

One particular guy in their Unit, Carl McCord, got on the bad side of the C.O. Carl could have been an okay guy, if he hadn't thought he was a bit better than everyone else. Carl had joined the war effort at the insistence of his father, who was a wealthy, well-known businessman in New York who had aspirations of running for political office. Having his son serve in the U.S. Army during the war would be good for his future campaign efforts. But Carl apparently thought serving his country at KP duty in the mess hall was beneath him and many a time Carl would goof around and throw food at others while they were eating. Henry and Joe thought it was childish. Wasting food was not something either one of them would ever do. Not when there had been many mouths to feed at the dinner table at home. Carl had never experienced hunger at his home, so he didn't care what he did in the mess hall.

The guys tried to ignore him and tried not to be around him much, but whenever Henry pulled his turn at KP duty in the mess hall, he inevitably ran into Carl. Once when Henry was the mess hall Sergeant for the day, Carl was being exceptionally obnoxious to a young man who was rather shy and quiet. Carl was hassling him, "You gonna' eat those potatoes? I like potatoes and if you don't want yours, I'll have them."

Anyone would think Carl hadn't had a good meal all his life by the way he acted in the mess hall. He was greedy and always took more than his fair share if he could get away with it. He'd take the last roll, the biggest piece of meat and anything else he felt he could get his hands on. Then, quite often he wouldn't even eat all of it. It made a lot of the guys quite mad and they wished the C.O. would walk in when Carl was pulling his act.

That evening Henry shared the incident with Joe about his day working at the mess hall where Carl was, of course, again harassing a young, shy private. "You should have been there, Joe. Carl grabbed the roll off that kid, Anderson's plate and took a big bite out of it and then tossed it back. Anderson took it all in his stride as usual."

"Carl, I don't want no trouble," Anderson said. He was several pounds lighter and several inches shorter than Carl, so a fight with him would not have ended in his favor. Henry continued, "But, Carl wasn't about to back down, he continued to harass Anderson and finally, I couldn't stand it any longer so I said, 'Carl, as the mess hall Sergeant today, I'm asking you to take your seat and leave the other guys alone.'

"Carl laughed, 'Oh, you think you can boss me around, do you? Just because you are the mess hall Sergeant today and the C.O.'s favorite, don't mean you can tell me what to do. I'll do whatever I want whenever I want. Besides I wasn't bothering Anderson, he doesn't want his potatoes and roll. Isn't that right, kid?' All Anderson could do was lower his head and shake it.

"So I said, 'Well, Carl when you are done eating his potatoes and roll, please vacate the mess hall. There are other people here who would like to eat their meal in peace.'

"'Oh so, you think I'm disturbing someone? Why don't you go back to washing dishes and leave me alone or do I have to make you?' Carl started to raise his hand as if to strike me, just as the C.O. walked in. The C.O. saw Carl's raised hand and immediately got in Carl's face. 'Henry, go back to your duties, I'll take care of things here.'"

"Wish I had been there to see it. What happened next?" Joe asked.

Henry continued, "The C.O. called the MPs and Carl was escorted out of the mess hall. A cheer went up as they hauled him out the door. The C.O. gave us all a look, but he now knew we were right about Carl." Apparently, there had been other incidents reported to the C.O., but the C.O. finally saw for himself the problem that Carl was for everyone.

Joe and Henry later learned that Carl had spent a couple of days in the brig and was on the list for the next transport out. Everyone hoped he was heading for the front line, but most likely **Daddy** had gotten him transferred back to a base on US soil.

Other than Carl being a major pain, most of the guys got along well with each other and they were kept busy with their duties at the hospital.

Henry and Joe looked forward to the mail and they continued to swap news with each other as they opened the letters. Henry shared Momma Collins's letter when she wrote that his sister, Ethel had married Jim Pearl. It didn't come as a surprise, but Henry felt bad that he couldn't be at the wedding. He remembered how bad Joe had felt when his sister had lost her baby and he couldn't be there. Henry's brother, Charles, and his wife, Pat, had another baby, Momma wrote. Was that six or seven by now? "I can't remember." Henry said to Joe as they read the letter. "She's really kicking them out!" Joe said with laughter and Henry just shook his head. Their friendship was certainly stronger because of those letters from home.

As the war raged on and the long days and evenings went by, the passes off base became even more important. Even if they just went to the **Red Lion** in the village, it was something to look forward to. But a chance to go into Leicester was a real treat. They sometimes would go to the cinema, but they most enjoyed going to one of the area dances. Seeing the cute British girls always proved to make for a fun evening.

Joe had been seeing a gal at home before he left North Carolina, but her letters were dwindling a bit and Henry worried that Joe would be upset. That didn't seem to keep Joe from flirting with the British gals at the dances so maybe it hadn't been a hot romance. Henry chuckled when Joe was flirting, but thought he himself wouldn't flirt so much if he had a girl waiting for him at home. Henry hadn't met anyone special during his younger days in Iowa. He was always busy working at the railroad and helping out at home, so there never was time.

The next few months were about to change that.

Chapter Thirteen

Needless to say, when America entered the war and their troops arrived in England after Pearl Harbor, the American servicemen were well received by the British families. Many of the Americans could provide things that the ration books did not allow. Things like apples, oranges, chocolate bars and nylon stockings were the most popular. Nylons for the women were a luxury and Dorothy and her sisters had often rubbed wet sand on their legs to give the look of nylons under their dresses before they went out for the evening. The sand would darken their legs as it dried and the girls would dust it off and draw a pencil line up the back to look like nylons. So, if the American guys had a female friend at the base who would get them nylons at the base commissary, they could have a supply with which to lure a cute British gal. Fruit and chocolates were good, but nylons made the soldiers very popular.

The summer of 1944 had seemed to last forever for the American soldiers and the British girls. Workdays were long and hard for them all. Dorothy, her sister, and her friends would go dancing at the Leicester Corn Exchange whenever they could afford it. The Leicester Corn Exchange was in the city centre next to Leicester Market. The building had been where farmers and merchants traded cereal grains up until the 19th Century. The large hall was used for many activities and weekends it became a dance hall. The bands would be playing the current music and couples and singles would come for a much needed night out. The entrance fee at the Corn Exchange wasn't a lot, but the girls knew that if they spent the money at the dancehall, then there wouldn't be much left for anything else. Occasionally, they would opt for a night at the cinema instead, but the dances were their favorite.

The nights that Dorothy, Joyce, Nellie and Cath did go to the Corn Exchange they knew that probably American servicemen would be there. All the girls thought the men looked so young and handsome in their uniforms. The word had spread quickly about the Americans' generosity and the girls knew if they were fortunate enough to be asked to dance, then maybe they would get some fruit or chocolates or nylons from these well-to-do American soldiers. Of course, the American soldiers didn't realize they were well-to-do and would have laughed if they had heard. But, they did know that having their extra rations did make them very popular and they were always ready to share things with their best girls.

Whenever they could, Dorothy and her friends would plan their special evening out. Dorothy's sister, Joyce, was a lovely young gal just two years older than Dorothy. Whenever Joyce wasn't out with her beau, Dorothy and her friends would invite her to come along, she readily agreed. Joyce and Ray had been seeing each other for quite a while and an evening out with the girls without him was a treat. And since Ray didn't care to dance, he didn't mind.

Joyce and Ray had been friends for many years. They had known each other in school and started going out shortly after they left school. Although Joyce was very fond of Ray, a night at the Corn Exchange was something quite different than their usual evenings spent at home with Mam and the girls or the occasional cinema. Ray's finances didn't allow too many nights out either. Joyce loved dancing as much as Dorothy so she always was ready to go too. Nellie was shy and didn't have much interest in dancing with the American service men or any others, but enjoyed the company of her friends, so she always agreed to come along.

Dorothy always thought Joyce put too much time into getting ready. She called it unnecessary primping. Many a night the girls would be late in arriving at their destination because they had to wait for Joyce as she made sure her hair and lipstick were just right.

"Come on Joyce, we're going to be late." Dorothy complained to her sister.

"Just a minute more, love, I want to finish my hair," Joyce answered. Although Dorothy thought Joyce's hair already looked perfect, her sister continued to shape it with her fingers making sure there was not a hair out of place.

"Joyce!" Dorothy cried. "Come on!"

"I'm almost ready, luv." Joyce said again as Dorothy let out a disgusted sigh. Cath and Nellie laughed as they watched the sisters squabble back and forth. They both agreed that Joyce took too much time getting ready, but then she did look pretty when she was done. Cath, Nellie and Dorothy looked good even though they usually just put on a bit of lipstick, ran a comb through their hair, pinned it up in front and they were done and ready to go. They too, of course, wanted to look nice, but they also wanted to get to the Corn Exchange early enough to get a good table near the dance floor. They thought to themselves 'Joyce is older than us so maybe she thinks she has to work a little harder. She really shouldn't worry even though Dorothy is the prettiest.'

The Leicester's Corn Exchange Dance Hall was already hopping when they arrived. The band was in full swing and they could hear it as they crossed the city centre open air market. The market was closed and the booths were fastened up for the weekend, but the smell of fresh fish and produce lingered in the air. A few workers were boxing up supplies as the girls walked by. The young men gave a whistle as the quartet of lovely ladies passed. The girls laughed and smiled at each other.

The hall itself was lit up brightly and the band had switched to a slow number that floated out the front doors making the girls anxious to go in. The hall was large with a lovely hardwood dance floor. It was waxed to a wonderful sheen and dance wax was sprinkled about to make it wonderful for gliding around during a waltz. Tables and chairs outlined the dance floor. There were lighted candles in the center of the tables which cast a soft glow on their faces.

Even though the building had been the farmers' marketplace in earlier days, the lighting during the evening dances was soft and romantic and the girls knew they would be invited to dance if they got one of the choice tables near the dance floor. Even if they weren't asked to dance by the guys, the girls knew they would get out on the floor and dance together on the fast songs. Everyone thought Joyce and Dorothy could really "cut a rug" in a Jitterbug.

As they climbed the steps and entered the front door, they realized the long wait for Joyce to complete her primping had allowed the room time to fill up. The girls always sat on one side of the dance floor and the men on the other. And the best tables were now taken. The girls had been giggling to each other in anticipation as they entered, but the giggles soon turned to disappointment when Cath said, "Oh, look, there's no table close to the band." The band was playing Glenn Miller's **"String of Pearls"** and couples were filling the floor.

"See, Joyce, I told you we would be too late," Dorothy grumbled to her sister.

"Hush yourselves, look, there's one over there not too far from the dance floor," Joyce pointed out, perusing the room for herself. "Maybe you'll get lucky anyway and one of those cute American soldiers will cross the dance floor and ask you to dance no matter how far away you are." She chided her sister as they hurried to claim it before it was taken by any number of other young gals who were entering the hall behind them. It was going to be an interesting night with so many attractive gals all vying for the attention of the young men there, especially the American soldiers.

Dorothy gave her sister a glare and Cath chimed in her agreement with Joyce to avoid any more conflict between the sisters. "Hmm, get lucky? That would be nice," she teased.

Dorothy looked at her friend with a suspicious eye, "And just what would Barney think?"

Cath replied sheepishly, "Oh, I didn't mean me. Barney might join us later when he gets off work, but I was thinking maybe you or Nellie would meet someone. Heavens, you didn't think I was talking about myself?"

Dorothy was happy that Joyce and Cath would still come dancing with her and leave their beaus, Ray and Barney at home, since she wouldn't have come alone. She so looked forward to their nights out. Dorothy laughed with joy as the band began playing one of her favorite tunes, Glenn Miller's **"In the Mood"**. She reached to grab Joyce's hand to pull her towards the dance floor. "Come on."

Once again, Joyce was busy checking her hair in her compact mirror. Dorothy loved to dance and they had won a Jitterbug contest together to that very song on a previous evening out, so she was anxious to get out on the dance floor again. She loved all kinds of music, but jazz and the big band sound were her favorites and she didn't want to wait any longer.

Joyce's primping was really getting on Dorothy's nerves. They had been late getting a good table because of her and now she was going to miss dancing to her favorite song if Joyce didn't quit mussing about with her makeup and hair. 'It was perfect already, so why couldn't she just forget about it and dance.' Dorothy thought to herself in exasperation.

"Joyce!" At Dorothy's irritated voice, Joyce closed her compact with a snap. She put it back in her handbag and took Dorothy's hand. Dorothy fairly skipped her way onto the dance floor. The sisters knew their Jitterbug routine well and before long people were stopping to watch them as they swung their way around the floor gliding effortlessly through their moves. Some of the watchers had been there the night the girls had won the contest and they enjoyed watching how easily they danced with each other to the swinging sound of the Jitterbug. The girls made it look effortless and the crowd applauded their efforts when the song ended. Dorothy and Joyce smiled as they walked across the dance floor back to their table.

"Oh, I love that song," Joyce said getting out her compact and checking her hair. "I remember when we won the dance contest to it."

"That was so much fun. I could dance all night. I'd just like it to be with a man instead of my sister," pulling a face at her sister.

Cath nudged Dorothy, "There's a couple of fellows in uniform looking you over."

"Yep, the one with red hair is really cute," Joyce chimed in.

"I kind of like the other one," Dorothy said.

Chapter Fourteen

Henry was sitting across the room with Joe and two of their other buddies. The C.O. had granted several passes that night, so Henry and his friends shared a table together. All the guys looked sharp in their khakis, but Henry had spent extra time ironing his uniform and polishing his shoes. His buddies were not always as diligent in their appearance, but Henry's mom had taught him it was important to look your best if you wanted to impress.

Everyone was watching the pretty English girls across the dance floor as they danced with each other. It was obvious they enjoyed dancing and knew each other well. Dorothy was the shorter of the two, so Joyce took the lead. They looked like the perfect dance partners and even though they didn't look a lot alike, Henry wondered if they might be related. He knew they had to be best friends to be so comfortable with each other. He smiled to himself and joined in the applause as the crowd acknowledged them at the end of the dance.

As Henry watched them walk across the dance floor back to their table, he felt intrigued by the shorter of the girls. She had lovely brown hair that shone in the lights of the dance floor. He was too far away to see the color of her eyes, but he could see the sparkle in them as she smiled at her partner while they spun each other around in wild twirls of the Jitterbug. Her svelte figure excited him and he wanted to put his arms around her slim little waist and hold her close.

'Do I have enough nerve to ask her to dance?' Henry was thinking to himself. He had never been known for his graceful feet on the dance floor and he wasn't sure he could keep up with this lively dancer, but how else was he supposed to meet her if he didn't ask her to dance? He hadn't been on very many dates and the thought of asking a girl to dance terrified him. Maybe he could just walk over and ask to join them at their table. Oh, but that wouldn't be proper. He would never do that at home and he certainly wouldn't do it in England!

Joe noticed Henry admiring the cute little brunette as she danced. "So when are you going to get off your butt and ask her to dance?"

"What? I can't dance like that," Henry moaned to his friend.

"Well, they will surely play a slow song sometime tonight. You can handle that, can't you?" Joe asked.

"Oh, maybe." Henry replied but his voice didn't sound very convincing. Several songs later, when the band did finally play a slow tune, Joe nudged him. "Now's your chance." When Henry just sat there looking longingly across the room, Joe said, "What are you waiting for? If you don't move soon, someone else will get to her first." Henry looked at his friend who was smiling and saying, "Go on, ask her".

With a great deal of trepidation, Henry decided he might possibly be able to manage a slow dance if he could just get his legs to get up and cross that large span of dance floor. 'Why do the girls always sit in groups on the other side of the hall?' Henry thought to himself.

On the other side of the dance floor Dorothy had been thinking the same thing about the boys. 'If they could all just sit around intermixed, it wouldn't take so long for the boys to get up and ask the girls to dance'. But it was a long-held tradition and not likely to change soon. So the girls just had to wait patiently to be asked. Oh, they could give a flirtatious smile in the men's direction that might speed up the process and a lot of the girls did just that. Dorothy felt uncomfortable flirting with a stranger, so she sat demurely hoping she would be asked soon.

Henry knew very well that if he was ever going to do it, he had to get up and walk across that huge dance floor. Joe prodded him, "So, are you going before the number is over or not?" Somehow he had to muster the courage. After all, he told himself, 'I can hold that pretty English girl in my arms, if I can just get the nerve to walk over to her before the song ends'. A panicky thought entered his head, 'What if she declined his invitation?' Of course, he knew that could be a possibility, but he would die of embarrassment if she did.

He began walking nervously toward her. The distance across the dance floor seemed longer than a five-mile run with a full pack during Basic Training! His heart was beating fast and his hands were a bit shaky. He suddenly decided against it and turned to go back to his friends. Joe saw his hesitation and waved him on with a grin.

The band was playing "**I'll Be Seeing You**" by Bing Crosby. Henry wanted to just say "Hello" and then "Goodbye" and retreat to the safety of his seat and his buddies, but that would be stupid. Joe's grin was encouraging him and with his last ounce of nerve Henry took the last few steps to Dorothy's table.

Not expecting she would agree, he asked with a slight quaver in his voice. "Pardon me, Miss, would you care to dance?" Henry was not a tall man, still only standing about five-foot-nine, but he had a full head of dark brown wavy hair which Dorothy noticed right away. She loved a man with lots of hair and the waviness of it made him seem so boyish. He was slim and trim and did look quite striking in his uniform. His pleasant smile and easy Midwestern drawl made him quite charming.

When Dorothy had seen the good-looking American soldier approaching their table, she wondered if he was going to ask her to dance. But then, he might ask one of the others.

'Pick me, pick me.' she thought to herself. Terrified, she hoped the thought didn't show on her face. Then there he was extending his hand to her and politely asking her if she would like to dance. She was thrilled, but also hoped he was a good dancer, for there was nothing she enjoyed more than to glide around the dance floor in the arms of a handsome gentleman, so she shyly said, "Thank you, I would like that".

Henry was a little shy and there was a bit of a lag in conversation during the dance, along with his "I'm sorry, I'm not a very good dancer." Dorothy replied kindly, "That's alright". Several more apologies for his awkwardness and stepping on her toes was the sum of their talking throughout the number. Dorothy's worst fears had come true.

"I'm so sorry."

"No bother."

"Thank you. My name is Henry, Henry Collins. I'm with the Army Air Corp stationed near here, at the Cottesmore Air Base," Henry said as the music ended.

"Dorothy Parnell. I live here in Leicester. I'm with my sister, Joyce and my best friend, Cath."

"That's my buddy, Joe. He drives the camp truck."

"That's nice." There was some awkward silence as they stood there on the dance floor. Henry cleared his throat as he led her back towards her seat.

"What do you do, Dorothy?"

"I work at the Wolsey factory sewing men's underwear."

Henry chuckled at the thought of her handling men's underwear all day. "Oh, I'm so sorry. Sewing underwear sounded kinda funny."

Dorothy was a bit offended but let it pass. "It probably does, but, it's a good position. I used to be a run-about before I was a machine operator."

"What's a run-about?"

"We kept the machine operators supplied and cleaned up the floor around their areas. My friend, Cath, was one too. We both started there when we left school. My pay helps out at home."

"I know what you mean. I send part of my pay home to my Momma."

"Have you been here very long?"

"No, my buddy, Joe, and I just got here."

Dorothy laughs. "Oh, I meant here in England."

"Stupid me." Laughing too. "I've been in the service a couple of years. We were stationed in Sicily for a while before coming to Cottesmore."

"Do you like it here? I've heard there has been a lot of fighting."

"Much better. Except for the dancing."

They were back at her table and Henry didn't know what else to say so he thanked her, and walked away. She was relieved that he hadn't suggested they dance again. She wasn't sure her toes could take it. She was also glad he hadn't asked to join their table. She wanted a man who loved to dance and was good at it. 'Forget about him even if he is pleasant to look at.' she told herself.

She had danced with several male friends in the past who were terrific dancers, but not serious boyfriend material. 'Why couldn't they both come in the same package?' she sighed.

Cath and Joyce were dying to know more about the good looking American. "So, how was it? Is he a gentleman?" Joyce asked.

"Gentleman, yes." Dorothy answered. "But not much of a dancer. I'm quite sure he won't ask me again since he spent most of this dance apologizing for stepping on my feet."

"I'm sorry, Sis. He was so cute." Dorothy agreed and was surprised at the feeling of disappointment that went through her. He had been so nice. 'Oh, well, there will be others just as nice, I'm sure.'

Across the dance floor, Joe is giving some encouragement to Henry.

"Goin' for a second round?"

"She'll probably say No since I stepped all over her feet."

Joe chides Henry. "You won't know til you try."

"Yes, but I hate rejection."

"Where's that determined Iowa boy I've come to know?"

"Ha ha."

A few songs later, Dorothy saw her soldier making his way across the dance floor towards her again and she knew she had to make a quick decision. How would Shakespeare put it? To dance or not to dance, that was the question. "Joyce, what do I do?" she asked her sister.

"Well, he is good looking." Joyce said. "Maybe he will get better. You could teach him later."

"What? Teach him? The way he dances it would take years and I'm not going to marry him! He's here with his buddy for a little fun tonight and that will be the end of it."

Cath couldn't help herself saying, "But, who can resist a handsome man in uniform? Go, have a little fun. You came to dance, didn't you?"

"I don't know if my toes can handle another dance."

"Better decide, look, he's coming."

She thought to herself, 'I'll just smile and politely decline. Surely there are a few good dancers here tonight. If I dance with him again, no one else will ask me. They'll think I am his.' She knew men could be territorial and she would be marked for the rest of the evening if she agreed to another dance with the same man, especially an American soldier. The British fellows were not always thrilled to have their girls swoon over the Americans. So when Henry held out his hand to Dorothy, she hesitated. Henry had a crushed look on his face. **It Had to Be You** was playing.

'Forget about those other guys and what they might think,' she thought to herself as her decision was being made. This guy was so sweet and he smelled so good, soap and after-shave mixed with a hint of cigarette smoke, so she smiled and took his hand.

They joined the other couples on the dance floor and again Dorothy's toes took some punishment. Henry again apologized for his stumbling feet and they both laughed. It was such a sweet, comfortable moment they shared. Henry was a shy, pleasant man so she would try to put up with his inability to dance.

Joe had crossed also and asked Joyce to dance. Henry looked over at them and found himself stepping on Dorothy's feet again.

"Oh, no, I'm so sorry."

So contrary to her first thoughts, she said, "Why don't we go sit down. Would you like to join us?"

"That'd be nice. Can my buddy, Joe, come too?"

"As long as my sister doesn't mind."

When they strolled back to the table and he pulled up a chair and sat down next to Dorothy, Cath and Joyce looked at each other with knowing smiles. Dorothy must like this soldier or she would never have asked him to sit with them. The girls recalled that she had rarely done that with previous dance partners although many had asked.

The night seemed to pass quickly as Dorothy and Henry talked and shared a bit about their lives. The sounds of the band and everyone talking seemed to drift away as Dorothy learned about Henry's family and his little town in the southern part of the State of Iowa, in the Midwest of the United States. She had no idea where Iowa was, but she knew it was a long way away. As he talked, she could tell he was a bit homesick and she was sure he must be very close to his family. That made him all the more endearing to Dorothy. As they talked, America seemed incredibly foreign to Dorothy, but listening to him tell about his family and job, she could feel a closeness to him she would have denied if anyone had suggested it.

Chapter Fifteen

It was two weeks later before the girls entered the Corn Exchange again. Dorothy hadn't heard anything from her American soldier and thought sadly to herself that she had hoped he would contact her, but he had not. She had given him her address much to the chagrin of Joyce and the girls. "What were you thinking? You know Mam would be mad if she knew you gave your address to some strange American," Joyce admonished Dorothy.

"He wasn't strange to me," Dorothy protested with a wistful look. The girls looked at each other and just shook their heads in disbelief, this wasn't our Dorothy at all.

As they entered the Corn Exchange, Dorothy looked around the room, hoping Henry had another pass and would be there. When they had parted two weeks earlier, Henry had asked, "Do you come here often?" Dorothy had laughed to herself, 'What a cliché!'

She smiled and answered softly, "We try to come every few weeks or so. I think we are planning on coming again in two weeks. When we get our weekly pay envelopes we try to put aside enough to have a night out."

"I'll look forward to seeing you again then," he had said. "I could drop you a note if I can get a pass. And when Dorothy offered her address, he had looked pleased. She realized that she really did want to see him again even though he hadn't kept his promise to contact her in the past two weeks. That first evening they had talked with each other so easily and she had hoped he would be there tonight. She cautiously looked around the room trying not to seem too anxious.

What she didn't know was Henry was just as anxious to see Dorothy again so he had put in extra hours for the C.O. and was rewarded with a pass at the last minute. Several of the guys were mad that they had to stay on base. But Henry and Joe had done the work necessary for the C.O.'s approval and reward. It wasn't always easy to get passes. No one wanted extra KP duty for two solid weeks and even though the extra work was tough, Henry thought it was worth it to see Dorothy again. Joe had washed and waxed all the camp vehicles to get a pass too as the camp's night driver the same evening since he wanted to see how things were going with Henry and his pretty English gal and maybe ask Joyce to dance again. Henry pressed his uniform and shined his shoes taking special care to look good.

"Hey, Buddy, you're going all out. This little gal must be something." Joe teased his friend.

"She is and I want to look my best. I wish I had sent her a note that we're going to be there, but there hasn't been time. I've spent every spare minute at the Mess Hall. I think they've been saving all the extra pots just for me."

"Well, they'll be sorry when they don't get to go into Leicester with us. I just hope Dorothy won't be upset that you didn't write." A horrible thought crossed Henry's mind. 'What if she wasn't there? Since you didn't send the note like you said, she might not have come.'

Henry was glad to see that he didn't have to worry for very long. He saw his cute, brown-haired, brown-eyed gal enter with her friends right away. He knew her in an instant and his heart began beating quickly. Joyce had also seen Henry right away and whispered to her sister, "He's here!"

"I know." Dorothy replied in her best casual voice. No point in getting all flustered. He might not come over. After all, she had not heard from him as he had promised. No need to let on that she would be disappointed; there would be no end to the teasing from Joyce.

Dorothy tried to remain calm, but her heart was beating quicker and she smiled at her sister as they walked slowly to a table close to the dance floor. Dorothy would have sat on the boys' side if she could have, just so Henry wouldn't have to walk so far to come to her. She knew how shy he was, but she also hoped that he would walk that distance to join them as she waited in anticipation. 'Just don't make the wait too long,' she thought to herself. In spite of her friends' warnings and her own better judgment, she wanted to get to know that handsome American serviceman. She didn't know what direction it might take her, but she wanted to see.

The band was playing **"GI Jive"** by Louis Jordan. Joyce and Dorothy hurried to the dance floor. Dorothy wanted to get in a few fast numbers before Henry came over, because she knew that they could spend the rest of the evening stumbling around the floor in slow dances. She made a quick plan to dance one or two dances and then ask him to join their table again. It was much easier that way and her toes would appreciate it.

Watching them twirling around the floor, Henry knew how much Dorothy enjoyed dancing so he kept his enthusiasm in check as she made her way around the floor first with Joyce and then Cath. He didn't want to interrupt too soon. He hoped she would ask him to join their table and if she did, she wouldn't get to dance like that with him. She looked so cute and he longed to hold her in his arms again. The band began a slow dance and Henry stood up and smoothed his uniform down and took a deep breath. He still needed to get that courage going to cross the floor and he didn't move fast enough because just then another fellow, a Brit, walked across the floor straight to Dorothy's table. Henry paused and watched as the guy extended his hand to Dorothy. 'Oh, no' his heart cried out. It was beating wilder and faster and he wanted to run across the floor and punch out the guy and claim Dorothy for himself. He didn't know whether it was a bit of fear or better judgment that made him hesitate and he turned around and headed back to his own table. 'Dorothy would not be impressed with someone starting a fight.' He also knew the British fellows didn't like the American soldiers taking their girls and any confrontation would not end well for either of them.

As Henry started to sit at the table, Joe said, "Look." Henry looked in time to see Dorothy shake her head and decline the offer to dance. Henry just smiled to himself.

Even though it was tough, Henry then waited through that slow song and again while Cath and Dorothy took on a fast number. He hadn't wanted to offend the previous fellow by jumping in immediately. He definitely wanted to avoid any confrontation that might ensue if the guy was really upset at her refusal to dance with him. He didn't want it to appear as though she preferred an American soldier instead of a British bloke. Neither of them needed that kind of trouble.

When **"It Had to Be You"** started playing though, it was the perfect song and Henry knew he had to get to Dorothy quickly. He looked for the British guy before he approached Dorothy's table and saw the coast was clear. He extended his hand and asked, "Hello again, would you like to dance?" Dorothy smiled that sweet smile that just melted him. As she stood up, he eagerly put his arm around her waist and led her to the dance floor. As they walked to the center of the floor, the British guy caught a look at them. It was a look of disgust, but he must have decided it wasn't worth a fight, he just shrugged his shoulders and headed towards another table filled with laughing girls. The first girl he approached readily got up to dance and Dorothy and her American soldier were forgotten.

"Good to see you again," Dorothy said.

"I was hoping you would be here." Henry replied. "I wasn't sure I could get a pass this week, we've had so much going on at the base. A new dispatch of wounded came in and every man was called to respond. I wanted to write you a note to tell you, but there wasn't time and all mail was being held anyway until everyone was treated. And I took on extra KP duty so the C.O. would consider a pass." He blurted out his excuse for not writing hoping she wouldn't be upset. The last thing he wanted was for her to be unhappy with him.

Dorothy's heart ached when he told her about it. 'What if he had been injured?' When that thought crossed her mind, she felt a tug at her heart. 'Oooh, Dorothy, careful, you might fall for this guy and then where would you be?' Even though they had just met, she felt a connection to him she couldn't quite explain. She hadn't yet thought about the real consequences of falling for this American soldier. She just knew she liked him and wanted to see him more.

When their dance ended, the band took a break and Dorothy asked Henry to join them again at their table. Dorothy had forgotten all about dancing while she talked with her new friend. He was so relaxing and comfortable to be near. He didn't put on airs and their conversation flowed easily.

"I think you would like Iowa. It's a beautiful state with lots of fields and animals. The farmers grow corn and we wait anxiously for the first batch to eat."

"You eat corn? But that's just for the animals." Dorothy had never heard of such a thing.

"Oh, no it's called sweet corn and it's different from what we feed the animals and it is so good." But Dorothy could not imagine ever wanting to eat animal feed.

"My Da has a big garden and grows vegetables and flowers to sell. Although, he doesn't sell as many flowers now with the war and all. And we rarely get any of his vegetables at home because they all need to be sold. It's been hard to earn enough money." Dorothy really didn't want to talk about how difficult things were at home, but Henry seemed so easy to talk to so she found herself sharing more details.

"Mam works part time at a clothes cleaner and Joyce and I help out from our jobs. I get a little extra when I work evenings at the Leicester Racecourse. Some of the players offer a tip if I've sold them the winning ticket."

There was no doubt in Henry's mind that she would get a lot of tips whenever she gave them her smile, but it also worried him that she might get other offers from the players and he wasn't happy about that.

They continued to talk about their families and hopes for the future when the war ended. It was hard to imagine what life would be like after the war, but it was comforting to talk about the endless possibilities.

Joyce and Cath could tell that Dorothy was indeed falling for this fellow and they hoped the handsome American wasn't just leading her along. Many of the Leicester girls had met servicemen at these dances and had bad experiences.

The American guys and the British soldiers could be cocky and some drank too much and several of the girls found themselves in uncomfortable situations. A lot of the American fellows would brag about being well to do and that they owned lots of land or ran a business, or had fantastic paying jobs back home. They had found it was easy to take advantage of young, impressionable girls. None of the British girls knew much about the Great Depression in the United States so whatever the guys told them, the girls believed, with the hope that they could get away from war torn Britain as the wife of one of these wealthy Americans. Some of them didn't realize the problems that could be waiting for them in America. Leaving Britain for some of them was to be the worst decision they would ever make.

Unlike a lot of the girls, Dorothy didn't care so much about being wealthy, she just wanted a good man who would be faithful to her and provide a decent home. She wanted her own home if possible and a couple of children.

As the music played, she daydreamed to herself about a little cottage in a small village away from the big city after the war was over. She wanted at least two children running around their little garden where she would plant flowers and vegetables. 'Yes, a boy and a girl would be ideal,' she thought to herself. 'I will work hard and I know that I can endure any hardship that comes along if my husband loves me.' So even if Henry wasn't wealthy, she just knew he could make her happy.

Henry's voice shook her out of the daydream. "Hey, you, where did you go? You were somewhere far away, I think."

Dorothy was embarrassed that he had caught her daydreaming. "Oh, dear me, I'm so sorry. I was just thinking about work next week. Mr. Garner said there were some new orders coming in."

She didn't know that Henry had been daydreaming about similar things not work-related either.

Chapter Sixteen

As the evening was ending, Henry had held Dorothy's hand and asked her, "Dorothy I would like to see you again."

"I would enjoy seeing you too, Henry, but we don't come to the Corn Exchange dances all the time. We have to save our money."

"Oh, I know, but we don't have to meet here. I can take you to the movies or we can just go for a walk. I just want to be with you."

Dorothy knew she wanted to see more of him as well, so after that second evening, Henry was to spend many a furlough in Leicester and later, at the Parnell home on Burfield Street during the fall of 1944 and early 1945. He put in extra work during the week to get those special passes. He didn't care if he got stuck with cleaning the latrine or peeling potatoes or washing dishes in the Mess Hall. He was willing to do anything that would keep him on the good side of the C.O. and the reward of a pass to Leicester to see Dorothy.

When Dorothy had asked him if he would like to come to her home and meet her family, Henry was delighted that she cared enough to share them with him. He knew by now that he was in love with her and wanted to marry her. He was nervous about meeting her father. What if her father disapproved of American soldiers? What if her family didn't like him? Oh, so many things could go wrong, maybe they should wait. It had only been a few months since they met but he knew he wanted to be with her for the rest of his life.

Dorothy had talked about her mother with love in her voice and on her face, but she hadn't said very much about her father. From what she had shared, Henry got the impression that the man of the house could be difficult. If he didn't like Henry, then where would they be? Surely, Mr. Parnell wouldn't stop him from seeing Dorothy, would he? Henry couldn't bear that thought.

Dorothy was also nervous to bring her American soldier to the family's home. She didn't know how he would be received by her Da either, but she knew that Henry was becoming something special in her life, so she asked Mam, "What do you think Da would say if I brought Henry home to meet everyone?"

"You know your father," Ellen replied. "He may not be very pleasant. He hasn't said anything too detrimental about the American soldiers, but who knows what he will say when he has to actually greet one in his own home. I guess it depends on what kind of day he has had. Tell me when you want to bring him and I'll be sure to fix Jack a good meal, so his stomach will be full and he can be relaxing in front of the fire with a cup of tea afterwards. That would be the best time to bring your young man."

Dorothy really needn't have worried so much because she had always known that Mam would be accepting, since she and Mam had long talks in the evening after Dorothy returned home. They would sit in the kitchen over a cup of tea and Ellen Parnell saw her daughter's eyes light up as she talked about her American soldier. Dorothy also knew her Da was another matter. She wasn't sure how he would react to her bringing an American soldier home. When he read his evening papers, he would comment on the war efforts and the American involvement, not always pleasantly, even though America was working hard to end the war.

Ellen had planned the meal carefully to have Jack in a good mood. She had fixed toad-in-the hole, with mint potatoes and his favorite Bisto brown gravy. It had taken a bit more of her household money for the week than she would have liked and she knew that she and the girls would have to manage on a bit less. It was important that Jack would like Dorothy's beau.

Ellen had reminded Jack of their visitor coming. "Jack, don't forget our Dorothy is bringing her fellow here tonight."

"I don't need to meet him," Jack grumbled as usual.

"Well, you will. Our Dorothy cares about him."

"He bloody well best watch out then."

"Keep a civil tongue in your head. She says he's a lovely young man."

"Mmmmn."

"That's all I'm saying. Be nice or you'll be sleeping all night in your chair again."

Grumbling once more, he waved her off. "I'll sleep wherever I please."

"You best listen to me." Ellen was determined to have Henry welcomed to the Parnell home in spite of what Jack might say.

Jack continued to mumble to himself. "A man deserves a bit of bloody quiet at night."

So, that evening after Jack had his evening meal and was comfortably seated in his chair with **The Daily Mirror** in his hands, Dorothy tentatively brought Henry in the kitchen door. Ellen greeted him with a smile and a hug. He was as handsome and slim as Dorothy had said and that lovely brown wavy hair did indeed make him look quite boyish. He looked clean and polished in his khakis. Ellen could tell that he took pride in his appearance.

"Mam, this is Henry."

"Welcome, Henry, come in. It's good to meet you."

"It's my pleasure, Mrs. Parnell."

"Oh, dear me, luv, call me Ellen."

"Thank you, Mrs. Parnell."

"It's Ellen, luv."

"Right, sorry."

"Dorothy, I'll mash a pot of tea for us all while you take your young man into the sitting room to meet your Da. I built a good fire earlier and it's warmer in there."

Jack Parnell was relaxing with his pipe in his old green chair near the fire in the small room that served as both dining room and living room. Henry took in the room with a single glance and could see that the carpets on the floor were as thread bare as Jack's old green chair. The dining table legs were scratched from the banging of six little feet over the years. Henry noticed that the walls could have used some new wallpaper or a paint job, but regardless, the room was clean and neat. He realized that Dorothy's family wasn't much better off than his own family in the States. He could also tell that Dorothy's mom took good care of her family and her love showed in keeping her home as neat and presentable for guests as possible in spite of their limited resources.

Ellen busied herself in getting out the best cups and saucers from the sideboard where she could keep a watch on her husband. She was ready to spring into a defensive mode if Jack was too grumpy. She had put the kettle on and she heard it starting to boil. She nodded to Dorothy to introduce her beau to her Da. Ellen continued to watch closely and listen from the kitchen as she poured the hot water over the tea leaves in the shiny brown tea pot. It had a chip in the lid from years of use, but Ellen loved it since it had been a wedding gift from her own Mam. In spite of the chip, it still made a good pot of tea. As the tea steeped, she waited tentatively to see what her husband's response would be.

She prayed silently Lord, be with Henry and Dorothy tonight. Give Jack your mercy so that he can be gracious.

Jack Parnell was engrossed in his **Daily Mirror** as usual and Dorothy was hesitant to interrupt. She knew well her father's temper if he was disturbed. He hadn't even looked up from the paper as they entered the room. But she was surprised to see him look up immediately when she said, "Da, I have someone I want you to meet."

The newspaper was still held up firmly in his hands and Jack looked around it with a vaguely interested look on his face as Dorothy stammered, "Da, this is my friend, Henry Collins. He's from America and is stationed at the Air Base at Cottesmore."

"I heard the Yanks had taken it over." Jack answered gruffly, but let his paper slowly lower to his lap. Dorothy held her breath as she waited to hear what he would say next. 'Please, Lord, help Da be accepting of Henry. He means so much to me,' she prayed silently. She had warned Henry that her father might not be too receptive. She braced herself and much to Dorothy and Ellen's surprise, Jack said nothing more. There was a bit of awkward silence and Dorothy cleared her throat.

"Da, Henry and I have been seeing each other and I wanted him to meet you."

"Tom Collins, you say."

"Da, it's Henry Collins." Henry looked at Dorothy and shook his head slightly to tell her not to push it.

"Good to meet you, sir." Henry said as he extended his hand to greet Jack. Without hesitation and without a return gesture of a handshake, Jack continued. "Yeh, what do you do with the Yanks at Cottesmore, Tom?" Dorothy offered Henry a chair as he answered, "I'm a Corporal with the 52nd Troop Army Air Wing as a Medic, sir."

"Hmmm."

"Da, Henry and I met at the Corn Exchange."

"Bugger that. Just wankers go there."

"Da! Don't be crude."

It didn't matter to Henry if Jack got his name wrong or disapproved of the Corn Exchange as long as he was alright with him seeing Dorothy. He remembered that Dorothy had warned that her father could be difficult and Henry thought it best to leave sleeping dogs lie. It did seem as though Jack Parnell might be accepting of him as Dorothy's beau. 'He must have confused Henry with the mixed drink 'Tom Collins', Henry thought to himself with a smile. 'Oh, well, I've been called worse.'

Dorothy's younger sisters, Paula and Victoria had been instructed to remain upstairs until Henry had been introduced to Da, but they had quietly, or so they thought, snuck down the stairs and sat on the bottom step near the closed door to the living room. It was drafty and chilly in the stairway, so they snuggled close to each other and strained to listen with excitement as Dorothy introduced her beau. They held their breaths waiting for their Da's response.

The girls could hardly contain their anticipation and giggled with each other as they continued to eavesdrop on the conversation in the living room. Ellen heard the girls' whispered giggles and decided they could now come in and meet Henry. She walked to the door and opened it and said in her strictest voice, "You girls might as well come in now."

"Thank you, Mam." They cried as they burst into the room and ran to meet him. Henry stood up to greet the girls and they stopped suddenly and just stared at him as they had never met an American soldier before. He looked so tall and handsome in his uniform and instantly shyness came over the girls. Dorothy looked at her sisters in surprise, they certainly had never been shy about anything before.

Dorothy said, "Paula, Victoria, this is my friend, Henry Collins." Having heard the exchange earlier between Da and this American soldier, the girls shook his hand vigorously and Victoria said teasingly, "Hi Tom". Henry laughed and said, "So nice to meet you girls. Would you like a chocolate bar?" as he reached into his jacket pocket for the Hershey bars he had purchased at the base Commissary just before he left.

The girls had already been excited just to meet Tom, but the chocolate bars were the glue to seal the deal. They thanked him and then looked at Mam for her approval to open them. Ellen nodded, "Go ahead girls, but mind getting it on your nighties." The girls sat down on the living room floor to listen to Tom and Da as they talked.

The girls were intrigued by Henry's accent. It was so different from anything they had heard before. "Tom, why do you talk so funny?" Victoria asked in her innocent eight-year-old voice. Ellen gave her youngest daughter a warning glance to not ask questions. "Victoria, don't be rude."

This was Dorothy's time to visit with her beau and Da, but Henry patiently answered Victoria in his America drawl, "Well, I'm not from around here. I'm from America".

"Does everyone in America talk like you?" Ignoring her mother's glare, Victoria inquired again.

"Hush, Victoria, I said, you are being rude to our Dorothy's fellow. You mustn't ask questions like that. Go eat your chocolate bar and mind getting it on you as I said." Ellen admonished her daughter. Victoria gave a frown and started to pout as she finished her chocolate in silence.

Paula, age fifteen, was interested in knowing more about the handsome American soldier. "Where do you live in America, Tom?" she said with her best grown up voice. Ellen let her daughter interject with her question since she was being so polite. Although she decided to let the girls stay for a short while longer, she didn't want them to keep asking questions.

"I'm from a small town in Iowa," Henry replied, thinking to himself that even though the girls were cute and nice, Dorothy was by far the prettiest girl in the Parnell family.

"Iowa, where is that?" Paula asked with confusion. Geography of the United States was not part of the British school curriculum, so she wanted to know more. Actually, she really just wanted to sit down and listen to this young man who talked with such a strange accent. She sighed as she listened to him talk. Never mind where he was from. She just wanted to hear him speak. She probably wouldn't understand where Iowa was anyway.

Henry continued, "Well, Iowa is one of the United States of America and it is in what we call the Midwest part of the country. There are a lot of farmers in Iowa who grow corn and raise cows."

"Do you have chickens and pigs and everything too?" Victoria spoke up again with all the fascination of an eight-year-old.

To hush her daughter, Ellen interjected briefly, "Is it like where we live here in Leicester as part of the Midlands?"

"Well, I suppose so, but on a much larger scale," Henry responded. "The United States is quite large. I believe the entire country of England could fit inside the State of Iowa where I'm from. Then, there are a whole lot of other states surrounding Iowa." Henry explained. "Many of them even bigger than Iowa."

"Really?" Paula and Victoria said in unison with their eyes wide in amazement. How could any place be bigger than England? They couldn't imagine any place in the world so big.

Henry continued, "America is across the Atlantic Ocean so you would need to take a ship to get there. First, you would take a train from Leicester to get to the dock at the coast, where you would board the ship. It takes about two weeks to cross the ocean before you arrive in the New York harbor. After that, you need to take another train or drive a car to get to Iowa from New York, which would be another two days. Altogether, it's about 4,500 miles from here."

Victoria's eyes were wide with amazement. Paula had no concept either of how far 4,500 miles would be, but she said with what she hoped was grownup understanding, not amazement like her younger sister, "Oh that's a long way." She still had no idea where Iowa was in the United States of America, but she wanted Tom to think she understood.

As the evening went on, the girls realized it didn't matter if they knew where Tom lived, just listening to him talk about it was fun. With more stern glances from her mother, Paula stopped talking and continued to enjoy her chocolate bar in silence along with Victoria. Victoria just sat staring at Henry as she slowly finished her own chocolate bar.

"Dorothy has told us some things about you, Tom," using the new name her husband had bestowed on Henry. To correct or contradict Jack at this point would only raise his wrath. Things were going so nicely, no need to stir the pot. "It's nice to finally meet you in person." Ellen smiled at the young man she knew her daughter was very fond of. "Tell us about your home and family."

"What did you do in Iowa before you joined the service?" Jack interrupted. He wasn't so much interested in what this American soldier did as long as he was truthful. He couldn't abide anyone deceiving him. Ellen and Dorothy held their breath in anticipation at Henry's response. Jack Parnell could interrogate anyone with determination if he wanted and Dorothy was fearful that Henry would not want to continue their relationship if he truly saw Jack as the overbearing father.

Ellen and Dorothy didn't realize that, in fact, Jack Parnell did have a concern for the welfare of his daughter and he intended to get satisfactory answers from this American soldier.

"Well, I'm not a farmer and I don't plant crops or raise cows. I don't even have any chickens," he said to Victoria with a grin. "But I know people who do."

Turning back to Jack he said, "I worked for the railroad, sir, before I enlisted. I did any other odd jobs I could find. I'm a good car mechanic and good with my hands. I enjoy working with machinery and with wood and building things."

"Oooh, what kind of things do you build?" Paula piped in again, in spite of Ellen's earlier warning glare. She hushed quickly though, as Ellen again looked sternly at her daughter.

"I've made some furniture for my mom and someday I plan to build my own house," Henry shared.

"Your own house?" Victoria exclaimed. She couldn't begin to imagine how anyone could build furniture let alone their own house. She had only ever known the row of brick Council houses on Burfield Street her family rented from the British government. She wondered to herself what it must be like to build your own house. It was positively unheard of! Once again, Ellen gave her daughters that mother's look and Victoria became silent.

"So you're good at plumbing and electricity too?" Jack asked almost accusingly. He had heard how the American boys bragged a lot about their skills and money. He wasn't going to approve of Dorothy seeing him if he was a braggart.

Little did Jack Parnell know that Dorothy didn't really want her Da's opinion and no matter what he might say, Dorothy intended to keep seeing her American soldier. She knew that Henry had not exaggerated about his wealth. She knew that he was a devoted family man from a small town who would work hard to support his family. So she kept her impatience with her Da's questions quiet and let them continue their conversation. She felt Henry was actually holding his own with her Da. Jack Parnell looked content with the responses.

"Well, no, sir, but I'm willing to try. I always say you never know what you can accomplish unless you try," replied Henry. "My family doesn't have a lot of money, so I'm going to build my own house with the money and materials that are available. I've been saving my pay here and hope to have enough when I get home. I've been sending some home to my Momma. I told her to use what she needed and if there was anything left to save it for me, I'm hoping there will be enough." Henry's response was direct and sincere. Ellen smiled to herself, 'Dorothy had indeed found herself a good man. But why did he have to live so far away? She was already thinking about what would happen if Dorothy decided to marry this American. Would she want to live in America?'

Jack Parnell was more impressed with this American soldier than he ever imagined he could be nor would he readily admit. He had heard some not so flattering rumors about the Americans stationed at Cottesmore. But he realized that perhaps not everything he had heard was accurate. The conversation continued for an hour during which Ellen served a piping hot pot of strong tea with some freshly baked scones. There was no jam to put on them like they used to have before the war, but since they were fresh out of the oven and still warm, jam didn't seem so important.

Just having the scones was a treat for the girls and Paula thought to herself, 'Thank you to this friendly American soldier who had come into their lives.' Paula and Victoria were ushered off to bed after they finished their tea and scones. The last remnants of their earlier chocolate bar were still on their faces, along with a smile at meeting Dorothy's beau. "Bye, Tom, see you again?" They chimed together as they climbed the stairs to the bedroom. Henry chuckled and bid the girls good night. "Sleep tight and don't let the bed bugs bite." The girls looked a bit frightened at that, but "Tom's" smile told them he was only teasing.

Henry looked at his watch, "I'd best be going soon too. My friend Joe drives the base truck and he'll be waiting, besides I'll be in trouble if I miss the truck back to the base."

The evening had gone quite well Dorothy thought. She always knew Mam and the girls would like Henry, but Da accepting him so easily was quite a relief. She left the men to chat for a moment alone while she and Ellen cleared the table and went to do the washing up. "Da seems to like him," Dorothy whispered to Mam as they carried the dishes into the kitchen.

"Yes, the toad-in-the-hole did the trick." Ellen said. They both chuckled and gave each other a hug. "The way to a man's heart I've heard, but Da calling him Tom was really embarrassing." Dorothy said. Ellen nodded but had a contented smile on her face as she thought, 'This Tom, or Henry was good for Dorothy and their family.'

In the living room the conversation was continuing. "How long you been seeing our Dorothy?"

"Only a few months, but I really care about her, sir."

"What do you plan to do after the war?"

"I suppose I'll return to Iowa. Probably build my house."

After the washing up, Dorothy and Ellen joined the men in the living room. Henry looked up as they came in. He thought again to himself that Dorothy was the prettiest girl he had ever known.

"Where does Dorothy fit into this plan?" Dorothy heard her Da say as she returned. "Da!" Ellen was right behind her. "Jack!"

"It's alright. Sir, Dorothy knows how I feel about her. I want her to marry me and come to the States."

"And what does our Dorothy say about this?"

"We've talked about it, Da. It's a big decision. We need time to talk more."

"Ellen, what do you think about her going off to America with this Yank?"

"I don't know. We've always been so close. It'll be hard." Ellen didn't want to think about it right that moment. She looked at Dorothy with a bit of sadness in her eyes.

Seeing the look on her mother's face, Dorothy said, "Mam, we can talk later. Please, Da." Jack just waved them off and went back to his newspaper.

"Good night, Mam. Good night, Da. Good night Dorothy and Tom." The girls were still listening in at the bottom of the staircase.

"Girls!" Ellen was getting disgusted with them and she headed to the stairway door as Dorothy walked Henry to the kitchen door and out into the little courtyard that separated their house from the neighbors' courtyard over the short brick wall. The evening had turned chilly and Dorothy shivered a little. She wasn't quite sure if it was from the cool evening air or the fact that Henry was becoming an important part of her life. "I hope my family didn't ask too many questions. They don't know any other Americans. I guess they wanted to know everything in one evening."

Henry saw Dorothy's shiver and put his arm around her. She snuggled as he pulled her close. The smell of his **Aqua Velva** aftershave sent a warm feeling through her.

"Oh, I knew there would be a lot of questions before I came. They are nice people, but then I knew they would be, how else would they be with a daughter and sister like you," Henry said with confidence. But a fearful thought immediately crossed his mind and he asked, "Do you think they approved of me? Your dad was tough, but he seemed to be okay with my answers. Does he interrogate all your boyfriends like that?"

Dorothy laughed, "Oh, no, just the Americans," she teased and went on when she saw the panicked look on Henry's face. "Of course they liked you! Paula and Victoria were fast friends from the moment you gave them the chocolate bars and Da even put down **The Daily Mirror** to visit with you. He doesn't do that often for us and never has for a gentleman friend of mine or Joyce's before. I think he might approve of you."

"What about your mom? She seemed to enjoy having me come."

"Oh, that was never a worry. I've told Mam all about you and she knows how special you are to me. Didn't you see her approving smile when you first arrived?"

"I was so nervous."

"I'm sorry for my Da calling you Tom. That was horrid of him. I was so embarrassed and then the girls had to do it. Poor Mam didn't know what to do so she just played along."

"Nah, he must have been confused cause there's a drink called Tom Collins."

"Well, I should have corrected him."

"No point in making him mad. The girls were cute. I kind of liked it."

Henry had taken the confusion with his name in stride and they were to laugh about it later. It was a good thing that he had accepted it, because the nickname was to continue later as Henry came to know Dorothy's brothers and their families. So even though his name was really Henry Collins, no one in the family ever called him Henry after that, the nickname "Tom" had stuck immediately.

Dorothy was still worried about how her family had responded to meeting him. "I hope they didn't ask too many questions. My sisters were talking too much."

"Oh, I knew there would be a lot of questions before I came. They were cute."

"That's sweet of you to say, but the girls were being a pest."

Henry pulled her closer to him and gave her a lingering kiss. "I love you, so much, Dorothy."

Her breath came quickly and her heart seemed to jump inside her chest. She knew that she felt the same way.

"I want you to marry me and come to America after the war."

Maybe meeting her family and their acceptance of him had been the thing Henry had been waiting for. Henry was thinking that now that he felt accepted by Dorothy's family, he could express the feelings that he had been holding back for weeks. He had known that he would fall in love with this lovely woman when he first crossed that dance floor to meet her but he had been wondering if her feelings were the same.

"I love you, Henry and I want to marry you too." Dorothy said with a quiver in her voice and Henry let out his breath in relief and took her into his arms for a longer kiss. He held her tenderly and rested his head on the top of hers, taking in the warmth and scent of her. She felt so good in his arms, he couldn't imagine not being with her forever.

They spent many evenings at the house on Burfield Street after that first evening and talked of their love and plans to marry and most of all, Dorothy coming to America. As they walked up the entryway as Henry was leaving one evening, he turned to her and said, "Dorothy, you know I love you and want to marry you. Do you feel the same way?" Henry had asked with anticipation in his voice and with such a serious look on his face that Dorothy wanted to laugh.

She forced herself to be serious and gave him a soft kiss, "Of course, I do." She wanted him to know how much he meant to her and the kiss reassured him and herself. She ignored the thought that his returning to America after the war would mean she would be leaving her family and going to America.

Even though they had talked about it and it had been on her mind for several weeks, Dorothy wasn't prepared when Henry said, "Dorothy, I have something to tell you. I don't really want to, but it's important." He took a deep breath." I don't know when I'll get another pass. Or even how many the C.O. will give out. Our unit is being shipped out to France. We just got our orders."

"Oh, Henry, no." Dorothy was taken aback.

"I know. The worst part is I don't know when or even if we'll return to England before the war ends. They say it'll be over soon. Dorothy, I want us to get married."

"Henry, I love you, but you're asking me to marry you before you leave?"

"Yes, of course. I can request a special pass from the C.O. and we can get married on Saturday before we ship out on Monday."

"Henry, I can't. I don't know. I love you, but I wasn't thinking about getting married now."

What had been another lovely evening with Dorothy's family was now turning into a disagreement. He knew this was the wrong time to ask her to marry him but with their orders to ship out, he had to do it now. He just hoped she would understand the urgency.

"I know it seems soon, but you know you're the only one for me. I knew the minute you walked into the Corn Exchange."

"I felt the same way, Henry. But, France? What happens if you don't come back?"

"Don't worry about that. I'll never leave you. Please, marry me?"

"What if you're killed or meet someone else?"

"That's nonsense. You know I'll never want anyone else."

"I'm sorry, Henry. I just can't right now. When you return we can make plans. I need time. How can I leave Mam and the girls? She needs me and the extra money I make. Oh, I don't know, Henry; it's too soon."

"Dorothy, please? I don't know if I'll even get to see you before we leave unless I request time to get married."

"Henry, we've never really talked seriously about me coming to America. It's so far, oh, I don't know."

"You'll love Iowa. It's such a beautiful place and I'll build us a house and we can have a couple of kids."

"That sounds nice, Henry, but we can have a house and kids here too; you know, close to Mam and the girls."

"But I'll be shipped home when the war ends."

"I need more time to think about it, Henry. I just can't leave right now."

"You don't love me enough?"

"Of course, I do, but I love Mam and the girls and they need me."

"I need you. Oh, Dorothy, look at the time. I've got to go. The base truck will be leaving. Say you'll marry me now."

"I can't."

"I've got to go."

"Will you write to me when you get to France?"

"Of course, I will. Every day. I'm coming back for you as soon as I can, so you be ready."

"I'll be counting the days until you get back." She asked tentatively, "Do you know when?"

"No, we just have our orders to move out in two weeks. I probably will not get another pass before then. There is talk that the war is winding down and we may be shipped back to the states after our tour in France. I don't even know if I'll be able to return to England before then. I'll write as often as I can," Henry promised and Dorothy promised to do the same. "Just remember our dance to **I'll Be Seeing You.**"

Henry waved as he ran up Burfield Street to where Joe was waiting at the top in the camp's truck with the other guys to take them back. Dorothy turned in tears to walk back down the long dark entryway alone.

Ellen had been watching from the kitchen window and she had a hot cup of tea waiting. She wasn't sure what had happened, but the happy look from earlier in the evening was gone and Dorothy was starting to cry. Ellen hurried out to meet her daughter.

"Oh, Mam, Henry is leaving."

"What, why? What happened?" Ellen couldn't imagine what could have gone wrong.

"Henry's unit is leaving to go to France. He wants me to marry him before he goes. I told him no."

"Oh, luv."

"I'm going up to bed. Can we talk more later? Night, Mam."

Ellen had been happy for Dorothy to have a good man such as Henry, but sadness had been creeping into her soul as she felt the realization that Dorothy's happiness could mean a deep loss for herself if Dorothy went to America. Ellen had tried to shake away the thought that she might lose her daughter as Dorothy had talked about her love for Henry. Now as Dorothy headed upstairs to bed, Ellen secretly felt glad that Dorothy had said no to Henry's proposal. She sat at the kitchen table and finished the cup of tea she had made. She let out a sigh then turned to continue straightening the kitchen and set out breakfast dishes for the morning. She hummed a little to herself. Jack liked his porridge first thing upon rising, so best to prepare things the night before. A rush of remorse came over her as she thought 'perhaps Henry won't return from France and I won't lose Dorothy after all'. Shaking the thoughts away, she headed up the stairs to her own bed.

Chapter Seventeen

Although their courtship had consisted mostly of dances at the Corn Exchange, the cinema, walks in the park or evenings at Burfield Street, there had been one splendid trip to London. Henry and Dorothy and Dorothy's friend, Cath, and her beau, Barney, journeyed the ninety-mile trip by train. The fellows had planned a wonderful evening for their special girls and had saved their pay and pooled their money to allow them the opportunity to take their girls on a nice trip to get away from the stress of the war and their daily responsibilities. Upon their arrival, they had gone to the cinema to see John Wayne in **Stagecoach** and then for dinner at a small pub near their hotel. A rare treat for Dorothy and Cath.

The train ride had been exciting. Neither Dorothy nor Cath had ridden the train before and they watched out the window as the train clipped along the track. The villages and towns sped by and the countryside was dotted with sheep and cattle. The green of the fields was deceiving, you would never know that just a few miles away, large cities had been bombed and people had been killed. The war seemed far away as the girls enjoyed sitting with their special fellows as the train moved closer to London.

London had been a site of many bombings and the girls were a little afraid of what they would see and they wondered if they might be in some danger. The war was still going on and London was a prominent target for the German pilots. Being with their American servicemen though, the girls had a feeling of protection, so they had vowed not to worry and to enjoy the day.

The movie had been lovely, sitting in the dark holding hands. Dorothy had snuggled close to Henry. Afterwards they walked to a small pub near their hotel for dinner. The dinner wasn't fancy, just a simple plate of fish and chips with mushy peas on the side. But to the girls, it seemed like a feast meant for royalty. They had been on war rations for so long, just to sit down in a pub and enjoy a meal that was purchased just for them was a treat. The pub was simply appointed and dimly lit, but to Dorothy it gave off a romantic vibe even though it smelled like cigarette smoke and beer. Several other servicemen sat at the small tables around the room with friends or dates. Henry smoked **Camel** brand cigarettes from America and he always made sure he had enough to offer to the girls. They couldn't afford to buy cigarettes themselves, but never refused one when offered.

"I just opened a new pack, would you like one, Dorothy?"

"Yes, thank you. This has been so fun, Henry. I never rode a train before and seeing all the villages go by was wonderful. And London is much larger than I ever imagined and exciting, even if it's kind of scary."

"I hope this little pub feels a bit more like home."

The dark, low, wood beams of the pub held the smoke down in the room and a grey cloud hung in the air, but no one seemed to care. There was a small combo softly playing music nearby and a few couples got up to dance in the tiny space that served as a dance floor.

The girls felt like princesses as the boys lavished them with Shandies throughout their dinner. They had chattered on until late in the evening. Henry had even asked her to dance to one of her favorite slow songs. It had been a perfect time, a day they wouldn't soon forget, especially Dorothy.

At the end of the evening, as they walked to Dorothy and Cath's hotel room, she began to thank him. "Henry, this has been such a wonderful day. Thank you so much for bringing us. The food was lovely and the cinema was delightful. John Wayne is so handsome. I don't want to go home ever again." She said wistfully.

"You know how special you are to me, Dorothy," Henry said as he pulled her close for a goodnight kiss. She readily returned his kiss and snuggled close to him to enjoy his scent. In spite of the smoky pub, his **Aqua Velva** aftershave still lingered on his neck and she rested her head on his shoulder.

She could have stood there all night, but she knew that Cath was already in the room and waiting for her. Cath had been a friend for a long time and they watched out for each other, so Dorothy knew that Cath wouldn't get undressed until she knew Dorothy was in and settled also. Dorothy didn't want to leave Henry, but she knew that proper English girls didn't spend the night in the same hotel room with a man until they were married. Her mother had taught that to all her girls, with the threat of the strictest of admonishments for any lapse of judgment. So a good night kiss and then in.

Although Dorothy had enjoyed the day in London, she was still quite concerned about the bombings that continued to plague the area. Air raid sirens would blare if the planes were sighted coming over warning people to take cover in the nearest bomb shelter. They had made sure they knew the location of the one nearest their hotel on their way from the pub. The thought of a bombing terrified Dorothy and she wanted to be awakened quickly if the air raid sirens went off during the night, so after their final kiss, she turned to enter her room and with one last gaze she said to him, "Henry, if the sirens go off would you come and knock me up."

Henry was taken aback since he and Dorothy had not been intimate up to that point in their relationship. He stammered, "Ssssure, I will." He left Dorothy after she opened her door and he walked away with confusion in his mind. Of course, the air raid sirens did not go off and Henry remained in his own room the rest of the night.

In the morning, Henry approached the subject carefully.

"Dorothy, what did you mean about the air raid sirens last night when I left you at your door?"

"What? I just wanted you to come wake me so we could get to the shelter together."

"Oh, no, I'm so sorry; I miss understood. In America when we say 'knock me up', it has an entirely different meaning."

After the explanation, Henry and Dorothy laughed about it, and it remained a story that caused a good laugh for family and friends on both sides of the ocean over the years. Dorothy had been appalled to learn what Henry had thought she meant. Henry, of course, would give a slight grin whenever the story was told as he always had thought he was going to get "lucky" that night.

Chapter Eighteen

The days seemed endless to Dorothy after Henry shipped out to France. She waited every day for the mail delivery. And once again there was some confusion with the language. The next misunderstanding wasn't quite as funny to them at the time. The letters were few and far between as Henry's unit was close to the front line and the mail didn't get out very quickly. Henry did have an opportunity to have his picture taken by one of his buddies. He had mailed that photo of himself all cleaned up and looking quite smart.

When Dorothy received it, she smiled to herself. How had she found such a wonderful, handsome man? She immediately wrote back saying "You look so homely". She of course, like other British girls, meant that he looked like the kind of man who would be a good husband and make a welcoming home for her and their family. Since it means something entirely different to Americans, Henry took some offense to the comment and wrote back, "Well, I know I'm not handsome, but I never thought you would say something like that." It took a couple more letters to straighten out the confusion. And it would be much later before they could have a good laugh over it.

When Dorothy returned from the front door checking for the postman, she sighed, "Mam, I haven't heard from Henry for the past two weeks and a half. He promised he would write. What if something has happened to him? Would anyone know to notify me?"

"Of course they would, but don't think about that. Joe would let you know, wouldn't he?"

"I suppose so, but what if Joe was killed at the same time?"

"Dorothy, you are being silly, why are you torturing yourself like this? If Henry said he would write, then he will. Stop thinking the worst." Mam knew that Dorothy was frantic to hear from Henry and she didn't want to think the worst either, but he had been so faithful to write and not having any news for more than two weeks did seem frightening. She had tried to reassure Dorothy, but no amount of words could make her feel better. She just wanted to hear from Henry.

The war was winding down in Europe and the letters had been few and far between. The sporadic letters were opened with anticipation and Henry spoke of taking her to their new home in Iowa after the war ended. Just how that would happen, Dorothy could not comprehend. She knew she loved Henry with all her heart and wanted to follow him to the ends of the earth, but to leave her family and go to America! She might never see her family again. That thought was positively terrifying!

When a month had passed without any word from Henry, Dorothy began to think he had changed his mind. She tried to convince herself that he had not been killed since there had been no telegram, but perhaps he had met another girl in France that he preferred over her. Surely Joe would have notified her. No, of course not, they were best friends. Joe would be accepting of any girl that Henry was seeing. These thoughts tormented her mind day and night. Hadn't he talked about marriage and taking her to America? He had never seemed like the kind of guy to lead a girl on, in spite of the rumors she had heard about the American servicemen.

The days seemed to drag on and on. "No letter today, luv?" Mam asked as Dorothy slumped into the kitchen.

"No, Mam. I don't understand it." Dorothy sat down at the kitchen table and began to cry.

"Oh, luv, don't cry so. Maybe it just wasn't meant to be. I didn't want you to go to America anyway. I can't imagine you so far away. You'll find a lovely young man here and we will always be close. Why don't I fix you a cup of tea and toast? You'll feel better with a hot cuppa in you."

Usually Mam's optimism would comfort Dorothy, but not where Henry was concerned. If she was trying to ease the pain of his abandoning her, it wasn't working. Why had he been so wonderful and sincere if he didn't intend to keep his promises?

The back door was suddenly flung open as Victoria came running into the kitchen shouting, "Dorothy, Dorothy, there's a telegram for you."

"A telegram for me, oh no," Dorothy cried as she sat down on the nearest chair and broke into tears. Telegrams were never good news. She hadn't had a letter from Henry in several weeks and now this telegram. She couldn't bear to open it.

When the letters had become few and fewer from France and finally stopped completely, Dorothy had tried to hold onto the memory of the last kiss they had shared before he shipped out, with a confidence she didn't feel. Now that confidence was completely gone. She couldn't bear to open it.

She thought about how Henry had been so upset when he told her his unit was going to France and didn't know when or even if, his unit would actually return to England.

Dorothy's words had stayed on his mind. "Luv, I'm not interested in anyone else. You know I love you, but...."

That 'but' hung in the air between them as they kissed their last goodbye. They both desperately wanted to be with each other, but not knowing what laid ahead for Henry in France, Dorothy was hesitant about getting married before he left. What if he was killed or seriously wounded? How would she ever manage? But hadn't Henry promised he would be back sometime, even if it was after the war? He had said then he wouldn't take "no" for an answer. Dorothy wished she had married him then. If he had been killed, at least she would have had the memory of their brief time together as husband and wife.

So, when Victoria had burst into the house waving the official looking document, Dorothy immediately had thought the worst. She had been terrified to read what might be inside, but when she opened it and read it, she laughed to herself........ just moments before the real panic set in

"Two-week furlough in England. *(Stop)* Prepare to be married *(Stop)*."

"What?" Mam looked shocked when Dorothy read the telegram out loud.

"This time I'm saying Yes, Mam."

"Why didn't he write sooner?"

"I don't care. He's coming now and we're getting married."

"But, in two weeks. How ever will you be ready?"

"I know; I don't even have a dress. What about flowers and bridesmaids? In two weeks? Oh, Mam. I'm going to marry a crazy man!"

Victoria gave her sister a hug and Mam started pacing around the kitchen. She was talking to herself and ticking things off her fingers.

"Well, I guess we'd best get started. Victoria and Paula can be bridesmaids. Your Da can pick flowers from his garden and we can ask your cousin Emma if she would let you borrow her dress. I'll stop by St. Alban's tomorrow. It will just be the family so no invitations to mail. I'll have Joyce go round and tell them."

Ellen paused to catch her breath when a thought came to her. 'How would she ever get Jack into a suit?' But there was no need to worry right then, there were a million things to do. And in just two weeks!

Ellen and the girls were thrilled to know that Henry was returning to marry Dorothy, and when Cousin Emma had heard the news of the wedding being planned with such a small time to prepare, she offered her used gown to her favorite cousin without a second thought. Dorothy accepted readily since she didn't know how she could have afforded a new one or even been able to find one on such short notice. Dorothy didn't care at all about the details. All she could think about was Henry was coming back for her! So she let Mam, Joyce and Cath take charge. All she wanted was to see Henry again and share another kiss. She had been longing to hold him again and in a few short days she would get to do just that.

The two weeks flew by in a whirlwind and their wedding was on a lovely June day in 1945, at St. Alban's church on Harrison Road in Leicester. The air raids and bombing from the early years of the war seemed to shrink into the past as Dorothy's family made their way to the church. The church was only a few blocks down the long row of Council houses, so they walked together. Ellen and Jack were in their Sunday best and Paula and Victoria had been primping and dancing around the living room in their bridesmaid dresses for an hour. Victoria continued skipping down the street in glee. She was going to be a bridesmaid! The dress was long to the floor and she had never worn anything like it. It made her feel like a princess. She was anxious to see "Tom" again. She had missed him coming to the house with his chocolate bars. But she supposed she would have to wait until after the wedding to eat one. Mam would never allow her to have it while she was wearing her bridesmaid gown.

Dorothy's Uncle Lawrence was going to pick her up early at the house in his car to deliver her to the church with her gown, where she could prepare and relax before everyone else streamed in. Lawrence Wade was Ellen's youngest brother and he and Dorothy were more like brother and sister than uncle and niece. Lawrence was always there, just like Dorothy's brothers to help in any way he could. Lawrence was fortunate to have the opportunity to go to university and had become a teacher, so he had a little more extra money, in spite of the war years. He had purchased a Hillman Minx for £165 and he was always proud to share time, money, and his car with his favorite niece.

"Dorothy, what are you doing? Lawrence is here to take you to the church." Ellen called up the stairs.

"I'm coming, Mam."

"Well, you'd best be hurrying or you will be late for your wedding."

"Henry has waited this long, Mam, I'm sure he won't leave the church without me having a ring on my finger." Dorothy laughed at her mother's chiding. As she hurried down the stairs, she wondered why she had worried all those weeks about Henry returning to her. 'What a silly prat I am,' she thought to herself.

Cath was, of course, the Maid of Honor, and she was waiting for Dorothy at St. Alban's when they drove up. "Oh, our Dorothy, you look beautiful. Henry will fall in love with you all over again." Cath hugged her dear friend as she got out of the car.

"I'm so nervous," Dorothy said. "We haven't seen each other for three months. Does the gown look alright? Mam had to take it in a bit. What about my hair? I haven't put on weight, have I?"

"Dorothy, Dorothy, settle down." Cath told her. "Henry will always love you no matter how much weight you put on. Remember, you want to have babies and you will probably get fat then." Cath teased her best friend, the best friend who would be leaving her very soon. Cath couldn't bear to think of it.

"Yes, but that will be worth it. Henry has said he wants children too, so I think he will be alright if I put on a stone or two." Dorothy hadn't been thinking about what would be coming after the service, she just wanted to be with Henry again.

"Oooh, I hope you won't put on that much weight, he might change his mind then and send you back to England in a packing crate." Cath teased as the two friends linked arm in arm and walked up the steps into the church.

St. Albans was a beautiful red brick cathedral built in 1905, an ecclesiastical parish of the Church of England and the perfect place for a June wedding. Dorothy had always loved St. Albans as a child and to be married there was the most wonderful thing in the world. The high Baroque ceiling created an echoing effect from their footsteps on the stone floor as they entered. The wooden pews had been polished to a high shine. The church smelled clean and fresh with the fragrance of newly cut flowers, and the organist was rehearsing softly in the corner. The candles were lit and they cast a soft glow around the sanctuary. Dorothy thought 'it's going to be the loveliest wedding ever.'

She remembered the many Sundays that Mam had taken them to the morning worship services when they were young. Da, of course, had never joined them. "Why do I need to go to church? You go ahead, say your piece and see how far that will get you. What will happen, will happen, and no amount of being on your knees will make any difference." Jack Parnell never minced words when it came to his opinion on religion.

Ellen knew better than to disagree with him so she hadn't pursued the matter further at the time and really didn't care as long as he didn't restrict her from taking the children to Sunday services. She wanted them to know the Lord and Savior. Fortunately, he allowed them to leave the house on Sunday mornings as long as he had his breakfast and was left alone.

Ellen was just glad today that he had not complained about coming to the church for the wedding. One never knew what he might say or do. He had even agreed to dressing up and for a moment Ellen admired how dapper her husband could look when he wanted to. 'Why did he have to be so difficult most of the time?' Ellen thought to herself. 'Oh, well, no matter, he's here now.'

As Dorothy sat in the anteroom listening to the organist rehearse, she recalled how she had always loved the music in the church when she was growing up. The songs had stayed in her head long after the services were over and she would hum and sing them all week long. Dorothy had a beautiful strong soprano voice and Ellen often wished she had the money to give her lessons. In actuality, Dorothy secretly wanted to take piano lessons. In Da's younger years and when he had been in a good mood, he would sit at the old upright piano in the front parlor and plunk out tunes on the black keys. The girls would sing along, 'I don't know why I love you like I do, I don't know why, I just do.' He had never been taught, it just was a gift. One that Dorothy indeed found later he had passed along to her.

The door opened and Mam's voice seemed to come out of a fog somewhere as Ellen snapped Dorothy out of her reminiscing. "Dorothy, why aren't you dressed? What have you been doing? Henry will be here soon and you want to be ready. I've told you once already today that it wouldn't do to make your soon-to-be husband wait. What are you daydreaming about?" Ellen chided her daughter back to reality.

Dorothy hadn't even heard Mam and the girls come into the room and when she turned and saw them, the reality of the day hit her hard. "Oh, Mam, I'm scared."

"No reason to be scared, luv. You will be the most beautiful bride ever and Henry won't be able to take his eyes off you. Now get dressed."

The borrowed dress was the traditional white lace gown with a long flowing lace veil that draped beautifully along the floor of the church aisle. Even though it had been worn before, Ellen had never seen a more beautiful bride.

The gown was perfect for Dorothy, all eight and half stone and five feet four inches of her. As she looked at her lovely daughter, Ellen was envious of that tiny waist. She had once had one herself, before all the babies. She sighed and prayed, 'Heavenly Father, Dorothy's life with Henry is in your hands. I want hers to be different than my own has been. Father, you are so merciful, stay with her during all the hard times to come. Thank you, Lord for listening to my prayers.' Ellen turned and smiled at her daughter.

Dorothy smiled back and all those weeks of wondering why she hadn't received a letter were completely forgotten. Henry did still love her and was coming back to marry her just as he had promised. Dorothy's heart swelled in love and anticipation. Truly, Henry had been a sincere, gentle man of few words.

Chapter Nineteen

A few miles away, Henry was traveling to Leicester in anticipation also. In his duffle bag was a small box he had purchased at a little pawn shop near Amiens, France. The box held a gold band nestled in the folds of soft blue silk for Dorothy's finger. It was just a simple band with no etching or stones, but it was wide and sturdy. Henry took it out and looked at it again. He wondered who had worn the band and why they had needed to pawn it. He knew there must be a story behind it somewhere. 'For what had they needed the money? Or was it a case of a lost love?' Henry hoped the ring did not carry a bad omen. He loved Dorothy with all his heart and this ring was the symbol of his everlasting love and commitment, and he didn't want anything to dampen that love.

"Joe, I want to ask you something." Henry had said the morning he got the news that he could get a furlough to go back to England.

"Sure, Henry, what do you need?"

"Would you consider being my best man? I know it means coming back to England with me and delaying your return home to the U.S., but you have been like family to me these past months and since my family is so far away, I would really appreciate it if you would think about it."

"Think about it? What do I need to think about? Of course, I will be your best man. I would have been mad if you hadn't asked me. What are friends and buddies for? Besides, didn't I encourage you to cross that dance floor to ask her to dance? You know I would have asked her myself if it hadn't been that you were so googly-eyed over her."

The two had laughed together when Joe hadn't hesitated for a moment to say "Yes," even though it meant he would have to delay his own return to the States. But for his best buddy, Joe didn't mind a few days spent back in England.

Now sitting there only a short distance away from his love, Henry thought the train was taking forever to pass through the little towns and villages as it made its way towards Leicester. It had stopped endless times and Henry felt his patience wearing thin. The crossing of the English Channel had been rough also. The sea was choppy and the small channel ferry had slowed down to keep the waves from crashing over the bow. Henry could hardly stand it and now the train seemed to be crawling along at a snail's pace!

He hadn't heard a response to his telegram and he hoped Dorothy had received it and was actually preparing for the wedding. He was being shipped back to the States in a week and he didn't know when he would be able to return to England if Dorothy wasn't ready to marry him now. Every letter he had time to write earlier had been filled with his love and plans for marriage. They had talked about it at great length before he left. He knew Dorothy loved him, but he also knew she was undecided about coming to America. He wanted to make her his wife and take her to Iowa. He didn't want to live another moment without her. He knew in his heart that Momma and Papa Collins would love her as much as he did. The thought that she might want him to remain in England had crossed his mind several times and gave him pause. He knew how much she loved her mother and sisters. She had worked for many years to help support the family and he knew she worried about how they would manage without her. 'But how can we live here? What kind of work will I find? Where will we live? There's no room at the house on Burfield Street. As much as I love Dorothy and care about her family, living in the same house would be a nightmare.' It all seemed so impossible to think about right then. He shook his head to erase those thoughts and glanced out the window at the countryside passing by.

As the train rattled along, he tried to picture Dorothy at the church as he put away the thoughts of where they would live. 'No use thinking the worst' Henry tried to tell himself. But the nagging thoughts kept coming into his head as the train carried him closer. He shook his head again and smiled to himself as he thought of her wearing a long white gown carrying flowers walking down the aisle towards him. 'What a sentimental prat I'm becoming' he thought to himself. He realized with amusement that Dorothy and her family had really become a part of his life for him to use the term "prat" instead of fool. He chuckled to himself as he laid his head back and drifted into a light sleep waiting for the train to arrive at the Leicester Rail Station.

At the church, Dorothy's sisters, Paula and Victoria's excitement was barely contained. They were to walk down the aisle before Dorothy. Ellen had given them full instructions on what they needed to do and how they were to do it. They were admonished several times not to have any last-minute mistakes. They were to act as grownup girls and not embarrass Dorothy on her special day.

"We won't, Mam, we promise." They said in the most grownup voices they could muster. They were all a jitter, but knew that Dorothy was counting on them. They hugged each other as the music began and they started their long walk down the aisle to where "Tom" waited for his bride.

Henry was not fully prepared for it when he finally saw Dorothy coming down the aisle towards him. His heart skipped a beat. He thought for a moment that he might faint, but took a deep breath and smiled at her as she approached him. She was a vision in white lace carrying a large bouquet of red roses, just as he had imagined. For a moment the rest of the world seemed to fade into the background and all he could see was this lovely woman who was going to be his wife. As she walked toward him, it seemed like she was floating across the floor like an angel.

Dorothy's heart too was fluttering in her chest as she walked slowly down the aisle towards him. 'What am I doing?' She thought to herself. The rush of planning for the past two weeks hadn't allowed her time to think about how her life was going to change. The realization was starting to come to her as she made her way down the long aisle, along the endless rows of empty pews in St. Albans' massive sanctuary, to the few in the front where her family and friends were sitting. She looked to the altar at the front of the church and there she saw Henry waiting for her with a smile on his face and all the love in the world in his eyes only for her. Any last-minute jitters disappeared as the organist continued to play softly as they spoke the words that would seal them together for the rest of their lives.

"I, Henry, take you, Dorothy, to be my lawfully wedded wife......... I promise to love you in sickness and health, until death do us part." Dorothy repeated the same words Henry had just spoken to her with so much love in his voice.

The minister gave the final prayer, Our Lord and Savior, I ask your blessing on Dorothy and Henry as they begin their new life together. Watch over them during their coming separation. Keep them strong in their vows. Bind them together with your love. In Jesus' name we pray. Amen.

Finally, the minister announced that they were husband and wife and Henry gave a sigh of relief. 'She was his!' He took her in his arms for a long tender kiss, and they walked up the aisle of the church with Dorothy's family and friends smiling and clapping. Henry's best buddy, Joe was right behind him. Henry was glad that Joe had been standing next to him in case he did actually faint. He hadn't needed to worry though, because once he saw her smiling face floating down the aisle towards him, he knew he didn't want to miss a moment.

So, in spite of the hurried plans, a borrowed gown, and the purchase of a pawn shop ring, the words Henry and Dorothy spoke that beautiful day in June would last them for thirty-four years. That pawn shop ring never left Dorothy's finger even after Henry's death.

Chapter Twenty

When Henry Donald Collins and Dorothy Luann Parnell had spoken those vows on June 5, 1945, the bitter days of World War II were ending. There had been little time for a honeymoon. A quick trip to London for an overnight stay was all they had to share. Just six days after their wedding they were separated when Henry went back to join his Unit again before they were shipped home to the States. He had to leave his new bride in England. Then came the long months of waiting for permission for Dorothy to enter the United States. It took several months for the U.S. Government to make the arrangements for the troop ships to transport the thousands of GI brides applying to come. The young girls came enmasse to the shores of America.

Dorothy was not part of the first wave of brides to arrive. She didn't join Henry until March of 1946 along with other anxious girls waiting to reconnect with their husbands. Their letters were filled with things about their daily lives and their love for each other.

My dearest sweetest, This Thursday I have been to the Legion Hall and had my supper. I slipped out after the meeting came to order as I wanted to write to you. I've been terribly lonesome. The picture you sent was very nice, but it made me feel kind of blue. I wanted to pull you right out of the picture. Do keep writing, sweet. I just got to hear from you. I'll write more letters, twice a week if you want to hear from me. I know if you long for letters like I do, then I'll write more often.

Hello, my darling, I was looking for a letter from you today, but it didn't come in this morning's mail. The last I heard was on Monday, so there had better be one from you if I am to get two a week. I wrote you twice last week. Did you get them?

Thanks for the five dollars, it will be a great help. You know Mam isn't working right now, so there isn't a lot of money coming in. Today, Mam had a letter from the coalman saying she had to pay one pound, seventeen before we can have any more coal. We were right out of it, so I gave the money to her. That was alright, wasn't it?

I went to the Belgrave Cinema, there was a musical on and you know how I like singing. In the picture there was some nice love scenes and it made me feel so romantic. Boy, if you had been here, I would have given you a rough time. I know you are terrible down in the dumps, sweetheart, but please try to buck up, it's not going to help at all. Each blue letter I get from you makes it so hard for me to do anything either. If you keep busy, the time will pass quicker. Honey, if I just knew what to say to you to ease your mind, but you know the situation. Until then, sweetheart, please take good care of yourself, I love you so much. Bye Bye, your loving wife.

More from Dorothy

Hello my dearest, I received your letter yesterday. You sounded so much more cheerful in it that it did my heart good. Please Hon, write like that always, you can't imagine how it makes me feel to receive one that you sound so miserable in.

Paula and I did a big wash and this afternoon we bathed and washed our hair and now I'm a bit tired. It is Saturday night and I'll have some peace and quiet to write to my wonderful husband and lover. I know it's hard for you to be alone, but the time will soon pass and then it will all be forgotten. I do miss you, my love.

Well, you must excuse me now, my sweet, as I've got a splitting headache and I'm going to bed, so take care of yourself, you are precious to me. Bye Bye, your loving wife.

The promised letters traveled faithfully back and forth across the ocean, and the time they were apart seemed to pass so slowly for them both. Henry worried that Dorothy would change her mind about coming to America. Her letters talked of family and her life in England. How could she ever leave them? He could almost feel the regret in her voice as he read the letters. Oh, he knew she loved him, but she was so close to her Momma and he could tell she was having a difficult time in preparing to leave.

Dorothy was indeed feeling the struggle. When her papers arrived telling her the date of departure, she had cried all night not wanting to tell Mam just how soon she would be going. It had been seven long months since the wedding and although everyone knew she had planned to go to America to be with her husband, the reality of it was drawing nearer when she would be leaving the house on Burfield Street and going to 'the ends of the earth,' as Ellen described it. There had been endless discussions about it.

"Mam, Henry's my husband. You know that. You know I want to be with him."

"Yes, luv, but why can't he come here?"

"Mam, be reasonable, Henry wouldn't be able to find work here."

"Of course, he could, why not?"

"Well, he's not a British subject first of all. He would need special permission to be here and to be allowed to work. It's all so complicated."

"What about your job? You could continue to work until he got settled."

"I won't need to work in America because Henry already has a job there. I will take care of him and our home and eventually have children. You know he's building a house for us."

Henry had told them a great deal about his family and his little town in Iowa. The house was coming along wonderfully he said, but it was so far away that no one could really imagine it. Dorothy wanted desperately to be with him again, but leaving her family was terrifying.

In the room that Dorothy had shared with her sisters, when she began her packing she realized the finality of her upcoming trip across the sea. "Oh, Mam," Dorothy cried. "I miss Henry so much, but I don't know how I can leave you. I'm so scared. I've never been away from home for longer than a few days. America is so far away, how will I ever manage? Oh, Mam, I don't want to go." Dorothy flung herself into her mother's arms as tears started to flow.

Ellen Parnell hugged her daughter, held her close and with an assuring voice she didn't quite feel, said, "Dorothy you can do anything you set your mind to. You always have. You are the strongest, most confident person I know."

Ellen wanted to help her daughter and ease her fears, but she couldn't help herself adding one more time, "You know I don't want you to go. I still don't know why Henry couldn't have stayed here or why he doesn't come back now."

"Mam, Mam, please, we've been all over that dozens of times."

"I know, luv, I'll miss you too, and your place is with your husband, but I don't want you to go. Henry had better be a good husband or I'll...."

Ellen let her voice trail off. She knew that Dorothy would be leaving so it was best to smile and accept it. "I'm sure you will love America. I promise I'll write to you every week."

"Oh, Mam, will you?" Dorothy cried feeling a bit of relief. "I'll write to you every week too." Neither of them knew the extent of that promise. It was a promise they both kept until Ellen's death more than thirty years later.

With the promise fresh on her mind, Dorothy was to set off to join 500 other war brides on the troop ship, **SS Argentina**. The journey started with a long train ride from Leicester to Southampton to board the ship, and Dorothy looked out the window as the train slowly moved along through village after village and town after town. The countryside was still barren from the winter months and Dorothy knew she would miss the sunny yellow daffodils when they began to bloom in March. She remembered all the times her Uncle Lawrence had taken her to the country to pick daffodils and bluebells. Lawrence had spent many days at their home with Dorothy's older brother who was close to Lawrence in age. Dorothy looked up to Lawrence and loved him more like a brother than uncle. The memory of those happy days and the smell of the flowers were so prominent in her mind that she felt a sudden pang of homesickness. The click-clack of the wheels on the rails made her thoughts wander back and forth between sadness at leaving her family and the exciting anticipation of seeing her husband again.

As the train approached London, Dorothy realized she was only about ninety miles away from home, but it already seemed like a thousand. How would she ever survive this terrifying new life so far away? Her mind drifted back to a few hours earlier as she had prepared to leave.

"Dorothy, come down, sit here with me for a while and have a cup of tea and toast before you go. It will be a long time before you get there. You don't want to be too skinny when you see Henry again." Ellen teased her daughter, hoping to help relieve the tension they were feeling. She hoped her voice would seem light and encouraging. Dorothy was still doing her final packing and checking her list. America was a long way away and she wouldn't be able to run home to get a forgotten item. 'What to take? I can't take everything. I'll have to buy things after I get there I suppose. Henry has said, the weather will be quite different in America, so maybe I should wait and see what I will need then.'

"I'll be right there, Mam." Dorothy called downstairs, but a few minutes later she was again so absorbed in completing the last details of her packing that she hadn't realized how long it had been until Mam called again, "Dorothy what are you doing? Lawrence is here to take you to the rail station."

When she heard Mam's voice, the realization slapped twenty-year-old Dorothy in the face. She was actually leaving! She was no longer a kid, she was a wife and her husband was waiting for her. It was very clear she was leaving her home, her family, her friends and her job. It was more than clear, it was frightening! She had even hugged sweaty, stinky, old Mr. Garner on her last day of work. He had slipped a shilling in her hand and wished her best of luck. He had been a dear to work for in spite of his poor hygiene. The memories were flooding Dorothy's mind and tears started to flow just as Mam entered the bedroom to see what was taking Dorothy so long.

Ellen saw her daughter's tears and went to hug her. Her own tears were close and she took a deep breath to hold them back. There was no sense in making Dorothy feel worse. It was going to be hard enough to say goodbye. There wasn't much else she could say, so she just held her daughter close and hoped the hug would give Dorothy some peace and confidence for the long trip that lay ahead of her.

Reluctantly, Ellen released Dorothy, "Come, Lawrence is waiting." They both struggled to carry the huge trunk down the stairs and out the front door to Lawrence's car. They were both fighting back tears, but fortunately, their goodbyes were short as Lawrence looked at his watch and said, "Dorothy, come on, we had best go. You don't want to miss your train."

"Oh, Mam," Dorothy hugged her mother again. Ellen pushed her daughter away gently and said, "Come, come, now my brave girl. Let's see that wonderful smile on your face. Keep that British stiff upper lip. I don't want to see tears as you leave. Remember, I love you and will write every week, so you won't feel alone in America."

As the car pulled away and continued down Burfield Street, Dorothy looked back at Mam standing on the front step with her hand held high in the air bravely waving with a smile on her face. It could have been as if Dorothy was only going to the seaside for the weekend with friends instead of leaving England forever. As the figure of Mam drew farther and farther away, Dorothy knew that Mam was crying, but that she would never have let on how her heart was breaking to see her daughter leaving the only home she had ever known.

Dorothy's sudden thought that she might never see her mother again sent panic words coursing through her head. 'Will Henry be good to me as Mam had worried? We really don't know each other very well, do we? Will he let me come home now and again? How will we be able to afford such a long trip?' He had told her that he wasn't rich, unlike so many of the American boys who had led the girls to believe they had money. These thoughts flowed through her mind as much as the tears flowed down her cheeks as they drove down Burfield Street. Watching Mam, her house and her life in Leicester fading away from her, Dorothy hoped she hadn't made a mistake. She prayed 'Heavenly Father, I'm setting out for a new life in America. It's frightening, Father, so I ask you to be with me. Guide Henry as he gets ready for his new life with me. And make the time pass quickly until I can return to see my family again.' Dorothy had the faith of a child that she had found a good man who would indeed let her see her family again.

The ride to the Leicester London Road Rail Station was short and Lawrence was quiet as they drove past Catherine Street School, Newton's Fish & Chips shop and on down past Brandon Street and across the bridge. He didn't know what to say that hadn't been said already, so he felt it was best to say nothing. He could see that Dorothy was now fighting back more tears as they approached the rail station, so he knew there was no point in upsetting her any further with idle chatter. He knew he would have a struggle to keep his own voice light and cheerful, so best to let things go unsaid for now.

When he stopped the car in the station's front car park at the north entrance of the huge Victorian building that had served Leicester's travelers since the mid-1800s, Dorothy jumped out immediately and before he could even get out to help her with her big suitcase, she was walking away. She blew him a kiss, then turned and entered the station. Lawrence sat there for a moment as he realized how sad he was to see his niece leave and silently prayed, 'Lord, watch over our Dorothy. She will need your care and guidance. Bless her with your love.'

They had actually arrived early and Dorothy had more time than she needed to ponder her future. The station was busy and she watched as people boarded and departed on the other lines. Once again, thoughts rambled through her mind. 'Am I making a mistake? Maybe I should wait and go later.' She thought of running back outside to Lawrence, but knew that he had already driven away. She was going to get on that train!

Dorothy noticed a young mother who was frantically trying to corral her young son as she pushed a pram with a fussy infant inside. The youngster was excited to see the trains coming into the station. He jumped up and down and screamed with fascination as the doors opened and people got off and more people got on. The infant in the pram only cried louder at the noise of the train engines and the loudspeakers announcing the arrivals and departures. Her brother's excited screams only fueled the infant's fear. When Dorothy's train arrived, there was no more time for thinking or people watching. She just had to board the train along with everyone else. She noticed the young mother boarding as well.

As the train pulled out of the station Dorothy was glad to be able to get a seat near a window. She wanted to look at the British countryside once more as she left. She laid her head back and tried to settle in for the long ride when she noticed a man sitting a few seats ahead of her across the aisle. He was eating something and Dorothy realized she was also feeling hungry. She had been so anxious to embark on her journey that she had failed to go down to eat the light breakfast of toast and tea Mam had fixed. As her stomach now gave a little growl, she wished she had heeded Mam's call. She then remembered and reached into her bag to find the cold chip sandwich Mam had slipped in there as she was climbing into Lawrence' car. "You'll be hungry before long, but don't eat anything you don't know where it came from," Ellen had cautioned. Dorothy didn't know how or why that would be a problem, but she knew that Mam was probably right. 'After all, Mam had told her, she was going to a strange country where she wouldn't know from where anything had come, so it was best to be cautious.'

'Oh, Mam, how will I ever manage without you?' The thought filled Dorothy's mind as the cold chip sandwich started to fill the void in Dorothy's stomach. The void in her heart was another matter and no amount of cold OR hot chips was going to help that.

The young mother who had boarded Dorothy's train was still struggling with managing the two little ones. The boy wanted to run up and down the aisles of the train and the baby was still crying. Dorothy thought to herself, 'I shall most probably be just like that young mother soon. But I do hope Henry is with me when we travel.'

Dorothy finished her sandwich and decided to leave her seat to assist the young mother who looked on the verge of tears. "May I hold your baby?" She asked the frazzled mother.

"Oh, bless you, luv. Yes, please, that would be lovely, then I can get little Henry here down for a nap. He's so excited to see his father. Ian is in hospital in London," she rambled on. "He was badly injured just as the war ended and he's been in hospital since. He had a weekend furlough just before he shipped out to the front lines and little Miss Betsy here was the result. Ian hasn't seen her and Henry doesn't really remember his daddy.... and, oh, I'm sorry to go on so." Tears started to flow down her cheeks.

"You just get Henry settled and I will sooth Miss Betsy," Dorothy told her. "I'm on my way to Southhampton to take a ship to America. My husband's name is Henry as well. He lives in Iowa where he is building us a house." The young woman smiled at Dorothy as she handed little Betsy to her. Dorothy sat down across the aisle and snuggled the little one to her breast patting her gently on her bum. Betsy was quite content to be held and soon closed her eyes and slept. The young mother did the same with Henry and he also drifted off to take a nice long nap. The two women felt no need to talk, they shared a common bond, traveling to be with their husbands.

The train swayed back and forth as it moved slowly between villages and countryside, stopping only for a few minutes to allow passengers to board or depart. The baby slept peacefully laying on Dorothy's chest and Dorothy looked out the window and let her thoughts travel back to her time with Henry before his Unit had shipped out to France. Even though they had talked endlessly about their future lives together, marriage and America, no definite plans had been made before he left for France. Then unexpectedly, the telegram had arrived and she had been caught up in the whirlwind of it all.

The wedding—there had been only those two weeks to plan it! Fortunately, when the day arrived the weather was glorious with none of the usual English rain. It even stayed warm and sunny for their brief honeymoon trip to London, but then just six short days later he was gone. The rain clouds had drifted in the following day and Dorothy's life returned to its normal routine. It didn't seem like she was married at all.

Almost a year had passed since that lovely day in June and with Henry far away in America. 'How can I prepare myself for this strange new home called Iowa without him here to help and encourage me?' They had written to each other every week, and he told her about the small house he was building for them and she knew that it would be perfect. Henry would put all his love into it, she was sure. She had always lived with Mam and Da in the rented Council house and the idea of having a home of her own was exciting as well as scary.

When the train pulled into London's St. Pancras Station, Dorothy kissed sweet little Betsy and handed her back to her mother. Young Henry was subdued after taking his nap, so Dorothy knew they could make the trip to the hospital just fine. The young mother gave Dorothy a hug and said, "You were a blessing, luv. You have a safe journey to America, now, you hear." And with a quick turn, she was off the train pushing the pram down the platform to see her injured husband. Henry skipped beside his mummy holding her hand. Dorothy smiled at the scene and thought of her dream to have a little boy and girl too.

The Southampton platform was further down the line and Dorothy had to change trains. St. Pancras was big and crowded. The Porter helped her with her trunk and in getting to the right train. She was grateful for his assistance. St. Pancras was overwhelming with the noise of the people and the trains. Even her thoughts were deafened by the confusion, but once she was settled into her seat she was able to lay her head back. As the train pulled out of the station she quickly fell asleep. When she woke the train was pulling into the Southhampton Station. She hadn't thought she was tired, but the stress of the preparations had done her in. Her mind was still whirling from the past week as she tried to decide what to take and it was filled with questions of what the next few weeks would hold, but she realized the train wouldn't be long in the station, so she quickly gathered her things to find her way to the Southhampton dock where the **SS Argentina** would be waiting to take her farther away from Mam and closer to Henry.

Chapter Twenty-One

Dorothy soon discovered that just boarding the ship and finding her room proved to be a challenge. The **SS Argentina** was monstrous and frightening. Its hull loomed over the crushing throng of women making their way aboard. It looked tired and worn after the war and its many crossings with troops. It had been a luxurious ocean liner in its earlier days but the war had taken its toll on it when it became a troop ship. Now there were hundreds of girls lugging enormous trunks up the gangway. Many were chattering happily while some were crying as they waved goodbye to their families on the dock. Dorothy suddenly felt very alone. She wished her family had come to see her off, but she knew that it had been too dear for them to come. The cost of the train ticket was far too much even for Mam to come alone. Times were better since the war had ended, but Ellen still needed to keep a tight household budget. So, Dorothy trudged up the gangway dragging her trunk behind her along with the hundreds of others who were excited to be going to America.

Her enthusiasm began to dwindle though as the huge ship seemed so confusing with stairways and hallways going off in all directions. Girls were chatting and giggling and shoving their way along looking for their cabin assignments. Dorothy knew she didn't want to wander the hallways for long. She didn't really want to ask for help, but finally she knew she would have to. She saw a gentleman in a white uniform who looked like he belonged on the ship.

"Excuse me," she asked the gentleman. "Can you direct me to Cabin 145?" Fortunately, the gentleman's job was to point the way for all who asked for directions aboard the **SS Argentina***.

*The *SS Argentina* was a US turbo-electric ocean liner. She was completed in 1929 as *SS Pennsylvania*, and refitted and renamed as *SS Argentina* in 1938. From 1942 to 1946 she was the War Shipping Administration operating troopship *Argentina*. Passenger capacity was 500. She was equipped to carry 450,000 pounds (200 tons) of cargo, of which 95,000 pounds (43 tons) was refrigerated. The ship had been built with two funnels but later during a refit this was reduced to one. The refit increased tonnage by about 2,000 tons.

On 8 December 1941 the USA joined the Second World War and on 27 December *Argentina* arrived in New York from South America. By 2 January she had loaded cargo and 200 passengers who had booked to sail on her the next day for South America. However, the War Shipping Administration intervened, cancelling her sailing and requisitioned her to be a US Army Transport troopship as she was one of the fast vessels able to sail independently when required. During and after the war she made a total of 56 troop voyages, covered 335,906 nautical miles (622,098 km) and carried at least 175,592 soldiers.

On 26 January 1946 *Argentina* left Southampton as a "dependent transport" carrying the first 452 war brides from England, Scotland, Wales, Northern Ireland and Malta, one war groom and 173 children to the USA in the Army's highly publicized "Operation Diaper's" European phase.

Dorothy hadn't known at the time that she was part of such a large group of war brides to come to America when the **SS Argentina** made her second "Operation Diaper's" crossing in late February. The United States government had seen to the arrangements. Her papers had been mailed to her with details as to where and when to report. That's all she had to do.

THAT'S ALL SHE HAD TO DO? She laughed at herself at the thought. Just get on a train for three hours, board a gigantic, terrifying ship to cross 3,000 miles of ocean and meet her new husband whom she hasn't seen for almost a year and travel another 1,500 miles again by train to a place in the middle of America called Iowa! To say that it was overwhelming was an understatement for sure. She had been terrified of just getting on the train at the Leicester rail station and now she stood here on the deck of this massive ship where she didn't know anyone and didn't even know where she was going. Her head was swimming and she thought for a moment she might faint. Taking a deep breath and summoning up all her courage, she followed the passageway where the Porter had directed. 'Here I go', she thought to herself. 'I've come this far; I can't turn back now.'

Cabin 145, if you could actually call it a cabin, was a tiny room with two sets of bunk beds squeezed on either side of the cramped space. Dorothy didn't know exactly what she had been expecting, certainly not a fancy state room like you saw at the cinema, but this cramped bare space was a surprise. She knew the **SS Argentina** had been a troop ship during the war, but having never seen a troop ship, she didn't realize just how stark and minimal the accommodations for the servicemen had been. She was beginning to realize that the American servicemen were not as well-to-do as everyone thought, at least, not while they were serving in the military.

No one else was in the cabin when Dorothy sat her suitcase down, but she assumed she would have other roommates since there were four bunks in the tiny space. 'Will I like them?' As that thought ran through her mind, she felt even more panic set in. She had shared a room and slept with her sisters all of her life, but never with three strangers! Even her brief honeymoon with Henry had not prepared her for sharing such a small space with three other women. 'What if they weren't nice or worse yet, what if they stole some of my things?'

Mam had warned her about being careful in strange surroundings, so the thoughts were running wild in her mind. She had vowed to be careful and follow all of Mam's instructions.

Suddenly, the door opened behind her and Dorothy jumped as another young gal about her same age struggled into the room with a trunk even larger than Dorothy's! She flashed a broad smile and introduced herself as Gertrude Kayes. She was shorter than Dorothy, a bit chubby, but her curly blonde hair and sweet round face immediately made her feel like a friend.

"Hi, looks like we are cabin mates. What's your name, luv?" The chubby blonde girl bubbled.

"Dorothy Parnell, I mean Collins," Dorothy quickly corrected herself. It was hard to think about her new name when she had been separated from her husband for so long. She thought to herself, 'I'd best get used to it quickly before I get to Iowa.'

After introductions, the girls decided on which bunk would be theirs. Dorothy said, "I'll take the top bunk if you don't want it." Gertrude readily agreed with a huge smile, "Thank you, duck, I don't like heights. I get all dizzy and sick. Shall we stay on the same side?" Gertrude asked. "I'm guessing we will soon have two more bunk mates." Dorothy agreed with a nod of her head. Gertrude seemed nice enough, but Dorothy quickly realized that Gertrude had the gift of gab and she hoped she wouldn't talk all the time. It was going to be a long trip if she did.

"Where are you going?" Gertrude asked.

"My husband is meeting me in New York," Dorothy answered.

"Oh, you're going to live in New York? You must be excited. I wish I was staying in New York. I've heard it is wonderful. Lots of things to do all day and night, it's even grander than London. My husband lives on a farm. I've never been on a farm and I hate animals. But getting away from England and my nasty brothers will be great, so I don't care where I'll be." Gertrude chattered on.

Dorothy thought about her own brothers and sisters and how she was going to miss all the good times they had together. Although there had been times when they didn't all see eye to eye, she never would have called her brothers 'nasty'. She felt even more lost at that thought.

"We're not staying in New York. My husband is meeting the ship there, but then we'll go to his home in Iowa. It's in the Midwest somewhere. He says it's a long train ride to get there."

"Iowa? Really? I'm going to Iowa too!" Gertrude exclaimed. "To a farm there. Do you suppose we will be close to each other? Oh, wouldn't it be grand if we could still see each other all the time?" Dorothy was a little apprehensive about a new friendship with this girl she had just met, but she did think to herself that having someone from England close by in Iowa could possibly be a comfort. 'As long as she didn't talk all the time,' Dorothy thought to herself. Little did they know at that time just how close they would be, not only in distance but also as friends.

"Yes, that would be nice," she said hoping her apprehension didn't show in her voice. Dorothy was surprised when Gertrude reached out and gave her a huge bear hug to seal their new friendship.

Over the next two weeks and the 3,500 miles across the Atlantic, the girls did become fast friends. Even though Gertrude talked constantly, Dorothy missed her family and friends so she was glad she had this new friend who was going to Iowa too. Dorothy thought to herself that divine providence must have made the arrangements and said a quick prayer. Thank you, Father, for sending me Gertrude. She has been my comfort and salvation during these past few days. I'm not sure I could have done it without her.

Their other two bunk mates were Paula Brown and Carolyn Knott. They turned out to be adequate cabin mates and of course, didn't steal anyone's things as Mam had warned. Dorothy felt a close kinship to Paula since she had the same name as Dorothy's younger sister. Paula was from Wales and had married her beau two years ago before the war ended. They had the chance to spend several months together before he shipped out. Dorothy was envious of Paula's opportunity to have spent more time with her husband. Shaking away that thought, she tried to remind herself that she would have a lifetime to share with Henry in Iowa very soon.

Paula was going to a place called Kansas and she said her husband was a wheat farmer. She and Gertrude shared stories about their husbands and farming. Both girls had grown up in a small village near the country and knew many of the farmers' wives in the area, but neither one knew what to expect in America. What would they do as an American farmer's wife? Surely it would be the same as England, right? They would probably have lots of babies and live a long happy life. They were oblivious to their idealistic dreams not always being the same as reality.

Carolyn had a different story to share. "My husband was a Sergeant in the Army and he runs a large business in California," she told the girls. "He says we will have many adventures there. He has a vacation cottage on the beach and the weather is always warm and the water inviting, nothing like the cold seaside at home. And the mountains are just a short drive from our big home near something called the Golden Gate Bridge. Do you suppose it's really made of gold? That would be brilliant."

With barely a breath in between, she continued, "We'll drive up to the mountains in Ben's big car to go skiing. He has promised we'll have a wonderful life in America." As Carolyn chattered on, Dorothy did agree that it sounded wonderful and she hoped it would actually be as wonderful as Carolyn had been told. It did seem a bit too good to be true.

As the girls settled in, they discovered that the ocean crossing proved to be arduous and many of the girls were seasick. The sick ones had made the mistake of staying in their cabins all day which made the sickness worse. Dorothy and Gertrude had listened to the Porter in the white uniform who told them to spend more time on deck and get lots of fresh air and to eat regularly, so they were fortunate that neither one of them had succumbed to seasickness. Their cabin mates didn't enjoy the crossing as much. They were not so diligent and therefore, paid the price. Dorothy and Gertrude felt bad that the girls didn't get out of the cabin much, but then they had made their own bed and now they were 'lying in it' as the old saying goes. "Good advice should always be heeded," Mam had said. Dorothy was glad she had listened to both her mother and the Porter.

The food, for the most part, was good on the ship and there was plenty of it. Both the girls enjoyed the idea of having second helpings of anything they wanted. The fresh fruit and vegetables were wonderful and there was always fresh meat. "I think I'll go get another plate of mashed potatoes." Gertrude said as they were finishing their evening meal. "I plan to make lots of them when I get to Iowa. We shall have a big garden on our farm where I shall grow my own potatoes."

Dorothy didn't know if Gertrude actually knew how to cook but the thought of making mashed potatoes herself was scary for Dorothy. Mam hadn't taught her anything about cooking since most things had not been available on the war ration books. "Dorothy, I'm sorry I couldn't teach you a few things about preparing a meal before you leave," Mam had said the day she left. "You know we couldn't afford to waste anything and I was afraid of what might happen if the meal was ruined as you learned to cook. I couldn't take that chance."

Dorothy understood perfectly well and had hugged her. "Mam, don't worry about such silly things. I'm sure I will learn. Henry has said Momma Collins is a good cook so she will probably help me learn about Henry's favorite foods and teach me what I need to know." She didn't know how plentiful things would be in Iowa, but sitting there aboard ship with all the food they wanted Dorothy felt a bit guilty eating so much when their families back in England did not have the same.

Throughout the long trip, Dorothy and Gertrude enjoyed spending a lot of time on deck. The fresh salt air was wonderful and Dorothy thought to herself, 'It's just like the seaside resort Uncle Lawrence and Mam took us to when we were young.'

The trip to the seaside had been fun when she was fourteen. It was the summer she had left school and before she started her job at the Wolsey. Uncle Lawrence had taken them in his new car. He had just finished university and purchased his Hillman Minx. He loved that he was able to share it with his family, although he was adamant that they were to keep their feet off the seats and not make a mess in his new car. It was absolutely forbidden to eat while in the car. Messy sticky fingers and food droppings would have sent Uncle Lawrence into a tizzy. Dorothy swore she would watch Paula and Victoria closely.

Mam had saved her money to rent a caravan for the weekend. They were to spend a lovely two days swimming, biking along the promenade, riding the Helter Skelter at the amusement park, and eating fresh fish and chips with mushy peas on top. The salt air and the smell of the fish, the squawking of the sea gulls, the shouts of the other children as they zoomed down the winding slide of the Helter Skelter drifted into Dorothy's mind as she stood on the deck of the **SS Argentina**.

Those times seemed like a hundred years ago. The war years had erased a lot of her memories from her younger days and now sailing across the Atlantic Ocean to America, it seemed her memories of even the last few weeks were being erased. England's shore had faded into the azure blue of the sky and was now a long way away, her recent memories of home were a pale blue as well.

After a few days out to sea, Dorothy found herself feeling quite homesick and felt like staying in her bunk and crying, but Gertrude encouraged her to come with her to the deck. "Come on, Dorothy, remember what the Porter said about getting fresh air. Paula and Carolyn are foolish to stay in the cabin all day. You don't want to get seasick too."

"I know, Gertrude, but I miss Mam so much, I just want to stay in bed and cry all the time."

"Dorothy, just think about how you are going to be seeing your husband soon and living the good life in Iowa. I'm so excited about living on a farm, I can hardly stand it. My husband, Bill, has told me all about it. He says the farm is quite large with cattle, pigs, sheep and chickens. He plants crops on over 300 acres of land. I think he must be quite rich." Gertrude chattered on. Dorothy listened and secretly hoped that Bill hadn't exaggerated his wealth. She did wish all the best for Gertrude and wanted

Bill's stories to be true.

She thought back on what Da had told her about the boasting of the American soldiers. Carolyn's husband's stories had sounded like he may have boasted a bit too about California and the Golden Gate Bridge. Was it really made of gold? She was glad she didn't have to worry about that. She knew her Henry was one of the good ones who did not stretch the truth and even though there was no gold in Iowa, she knew he was building them a lovely home.

Paula had been relatively quiet and closed about her life after their first day when they had introduced themselves and shared where they were going. The girls had tried several times to make friends and to get her to open up, but she was suffering not only from the seasickness, but a severe case of homesickness as well and didn't want to talk about it. She refused to leave her bunk most of the trip and after several days of coaxing, Gertrude sadly gave up and left Paula to be by herself.

Dorothy too had wanted to help Paula just as much as if she had been her own little sister, so she approached the bunk where Paula laid looking pale and gaunt. "Paula, how are you feeling? Don't you think you would be better if you came with us up to the deck? The Porter said you wouldn't get sick if you have fresh air and eat something regularly." Paula rolled over holding her stomach and just cried some more. She shook her head and waved Dorothy away. Dorothy knew how she must be feeling at leaving her home and family. She had felt that way too and thank goodness Gertrude's bubbly personality had kept Dorothy from sinking into the chasm of homesickness where she might never have gotten out.

"Are you sure, luv? This cabin is so stuffy, won't you come up top with us?" Paula shook her head and waved Dorothy away, so Dorothy gave up as well and left Paula to her misery and slipped out of the cabin for some fresh sea air of her own.

As the days dragged on, the ocean seemed to go on forever too. Dorothy leaned over the deck railing and looked out hoping she would see land soon. She wondered if Henry would be there waiting for her. 'What if he had changed his mind? Oh, my, why had that thought just entered my head? Of course, he would be there.' She thought again about Gertrude's husband, Bill, and wondered and hoped again that he would be the husband that Gertrude was anticipating.

The long crossing gave all the girls too much time to think. To think about their future in America with their husbands and to think about their past and what they were leaving behind in England. It was hard to keep the thoughts clear.

After two long weeks, the **SS Argentina** approached the New York harbor, the loudspeakers began explaining the docking procedures. Gertrude and Dorothy stood on the deck waiting to disembark. The Statue of Liberty stood majestically nearby with her arm in the air as if waving to the newcomers and the girls were amazed. "Oh, Dorothy isn't she huge and magnificent. I had heard about it, but I didn't know what to expect." Gertrude exclaimed. She grabbed Dorothy's hand, "Don't leave me, I'm afraid to do this alone." Dorothy was surprised to hear that from bubbly Gertrude who had chattered so much and encouraged everyone else throughout the entire trip and now she needed Dorothy's support?

"I'm right here, Gertrude. We will stay together all the way. I don't want to go through the long processing at Ellis Island alone either. I've heard it's not very pleasant." Dorothy told her. The girls clutched hands as they watched the ship pull into the dock. The little tugboats that guided them in were dwarfed by the **SS Argentina**. Dorothy looked at Gertrude and realized their friendship was a much-needed comfort for both of them. She sincerely hoped it would continue when they got settled in Iowa. She hoped Bill's farm wasn't too far from Henry and his family and that they could, in fact, see each other regularly. If not, maybe they would at least write to each other.

The docking process seemed to take forever, but finally the **SS Argentina** was securely settled and the girls lugged their possessions onto barges that would take them to Ellis Island where the immigrants were tagged with information from the ship's registry and passed through long lines for medical and legal inspections to determine their eligibility to enter the United States. The process for the war brides was not as strenuous as it had been for earlier immigrants to the U.S., but it was still a tedious undertaking.

Previously the doctors had checked the immigrants who arrived in America before the war for more than sixty diseases and disabilities. One of the diseases of particular concern had been trachoma, a contagious eye condition. To check for trachoma, in the early years of Ellis Island, the examiner used a buttonhook to turn each immigrant's eyelids inside out. Stories of the procedure being particularly painful, terrified the young war brides. Fortunately, they did not have to succumb to that medical exam.

Conditions were not always the best with so many people being processed through Ellis Island, but the food was plentiful, despite various opinions as to its quality. A typical meal might include one or more of the following, beef stew, potatoes, bread, herring, or baked beans and stewed prunes. Bananas, sandwiches, and even ice cream were offered. Dorothy and Gertrude had never seen so much readily available food on the ship and now at Ellis Island. America was indeed the land of opportunity. Each time they sat down to eat, they couldn't help but think again about how the war rations had never provided such feasts for their families at home.

The girls were relieved that after processing papers and checking records, they were told they were approved to leave the island. They didn't have much money and weren't sure how long it would be before they would have another meal. When they were told that packaged food could also be purchased before leaving, they both got a small bundle. They had enjoyed a big breakfast that morning and hoped that with their purchase, it would tide them over.

Dorothy was relieved to know that Henry was to meet her in New York. It meant she didn't have to stay at Ellis Island for long. Gertrude's husband, Bill, was meeting her also. As the girls stood on the dock looking for their husbands, Gertrude said, "Dorothy, you are wonderful. How will I ever get along without you? We simply must get together." Gertrude exclaimed as usual with barely a breath in between, "Bill will probably be busy on the farm, but I will write you to come for a visit as soon as I can."

Dorothy and Gertrude said their final goodbyes and promised to keep in touch when they both got settled into their new homes in Iowa. Dorothy gave her new friend a hug and a wave as Gertrude ran to meet Bill who was waving madly a few yards away.

Dorothy was feeling quite alone standing there at the dock with her big trunk holding all the possessions she had in the world, when she looked around and suddenly there was Henry coming towards her beaming with a smile as large as the moon! She threw her arms around his neck as he planted a huge kiss on her. The last few lonely months seemed to fade away as she realized how happy she was to see him. She enthusiastically returned the kiss and chuckled to herself as to how she planned to make good on a promise she had made in one of her letters.

My Dearest Henry. I cannot wait to see you and get you in a corner. I will keep kissing you and kissing you until you shout 'uncle'. So you had better be ready. If I were there now you wouldn't get away from me. It won't be you who will do all the grabbing, so watch out!........

Chapter Twenty-Two

Bertha Collins had been relieved to learn that her youngest son, Henry, had been selected to be a medic in the Army Air Corp. Even though he was shipped out for a tour of duty in Europe, she felt that as a medic he might not ever have to see the front line. She had prayed, 'Father, thank you for answering my prayer for Henry's safety. Keep watching over him until he returns home.' She knew with his gentle manner and sympathetic heart he would make a good medic. She hoped it would keep him out of harm's way and he would return safely to her and the family when the war ended.

Henry had faithfully written letters home and sent money as he had promised. Bertha enjoyed hearing from him and knowing about his daily work. She laughed about all the good times he and Joe shared. She almost felt like she knew Joe from the things Henry had written. She was pleased that he and Joe had received passes to go into Leicester and have some fun away from the turmoil of the war. She was sure those evenings out had been much needed. She was a bit concerned though when he began telling her about the wonderful girl he had met. She could tell from the way he spoke about her that she was becoming very special to him. She truly wanted Henry to find happiness, but she worried about it being with someone so far away. What would happen when the war ended? She had been secretly happy that Dorothy had declined Henry's proposal of marriage before he left for France. She felt like it was for the best and that Henry would forget about her when the war was over.

So when Momma Collins received the letter from Henry saying he would be bringing home a British bride, she was deeply saddened and terrified. She was thrilled that Henry had fallen in love, but was disappointed that he had married while still in England without telling her. She had hoped to have a family wedding here at home someday. Now, she struggled to understand how she would accept this woman she had never met being a part of Henry's life. She also worried whether Dorothy would "fit in" with the family and her fears proved to be true at first. There had been so many unpleasant comments from everyone when Bertha told them.

Of course, it was no surprise the family didn't know what to think. 'How were they to relate to a young, foreign girl? Did she even speak English?' Most of them didn't even know where England was! The family was still grieving over the loss of Randall. Even though he had been a hero, his not returning and now Henry coming home with a British bride did not sit well with everyone. Even though they knew it was unreasonable to think; they wanted to know why she was coming to live with them when young Randall would never return to marry and have his family. It wasn't fair! It just didn't seem right and their grief would make Dorothy's early years in her new home quite difficult as well as being strange.

Bertha tried to intervene whenever possible and some of the family attempted to be friendly, but most of them just kept their distance at first. Henry's oldest sister, Ren, didn't even try to get along. She made it quite plain that Dorothy was an outsider. Bertha knew that the family was still in shock over Randall's death and it would be up to her to help Dorothy become a part of the family. If Henry loved her, that was enough for Bertha, so she was determined to make it work in spite of Ren's grief over losing her youngest son. But no matter how hard she tried, Bertha couldn't make Ren understand that she shouldn't take it out on Dorothy.

Of course, Bertha had her own doubts and although she kept them to herself, they constantly plagued her mind. Would this young girl know how to "keep house" and cook? And how would she manage having babies here in a strange country without her own momma with her? Would she cry a lot with homesickness? And would everyone be able to understand her accent?' Momma Collins knew that Henry wanted a family, so the questions and doubts had flooded Bertha's thoughts as she prepared for Dorothy's arrival. It was going to be tough enough for her to become part of the close-knit Collins family and her talking funny wouldn't help. 'Oh, my, how will we manage?'

One of Bertha's most dreaded questions kept returning to her mind. 'Did this young foreign girl love Henry and would she take good care of him?' She felt in her heart that Dorothy must truly love him or she wouldn't have left her family so far away, not knowing whether she would ever see them again. Bertha remembered how scared she had been when Henry left for the service, not knowing if she would see him again. But Dorothy was so young. 'How would she adjust here?'

She pondered this question as she waited for Dorothy's arrival. In spite of her fears, Bertha was determined to share her home and family with this stranger and help her become a part of a new life in America. She watched with pride as Henry began building their new home in preparation for his new bride.

Bertha needn't have worried herself so. In spite of Ren's refusal to accept Dorothy, after a short while Fanny, Randall's sister and Ethel, Henry's sister, welcomed Dorothy into the family, much to Ren's chagrin. Fanny and Ethel were close in age and took young Dorothy under their wings. Later, as they all had children close in age, their friendship grew as Dorothy began to become a part of the Collins clan.

Bertha Collins was a matronly big-busted woman who wore an apron over her house dress and whistled while she worked. She always seemed to be jolly. She baked bread and pies every day for her family as well as washing what had seemed like endless amounts of clothes to be hung out in the sun to dry when the children were younger. She had always thought, 'I don't know how those boys get so dirty all the time. Why couldn't they have been more like sweet little Ethel?' Bertha would never have shared those complaining words out loud because she loved her family, but it had been a relief when the older ones had left to just have Ethel, Papa Collins and herself to care for. And with Henry gone, the past few years her life had been much easier. Now, she knew her family would be growing again with Dorothy's arrival and perhaps future grandchildren. The thought was a bit frightening, but she told herself to look forward again to having a big family to care for regardless of how much work would ensue. She just hoped she had the strength and wisdom for it.

Henry's sister, Ethel was a quiet girl. Even though she was four years older than Henry, they had been close since they were the last to leave home. Ethel had cried for weeks after Henry left. Momma Collins had written to Henry during his Basic Training asking him to write a special letter to Ethel to ease her pain at saying goodbye to her baby brother. Henry had been eager to comply. Even though he didn't want to admit it to anyone or himself, he had missed Ethel and Momma and Papa too. Life was going on in Iowa without him. The homesickness was strong when Ethel married Jim Pearl while Henry was gone. They had bought a little house only a few blocks away so Henry knew that Ethel and Momma would remain close, but not being at her wedding had been hard for Henry. Ethel and Jim already had one daughter and another on the way when Henry returned. The sadness of missing out on his family's growing stayed with him long after he arrived home.

Chapter Twenty-Three

During the long months they were separated, the letters never stopped. Henry waited "patiently" for Dorothy's letters to arrive and she anxiously awaited his. Waiting for Dorothy to come to America, his sadness sometimes would outweigh everything. Even though he had the new house to build, his focus always returned to Dorothy and how much he missed her.

From Henry:
My Dearest. Today is Sunday and here I am writing to the sweetest little woman I know. I just received your letter and boy it was so good to get it. I felt so blue Friday, I just wanted to sit down and cry. Then the mailman came on Saturday and gave me your letter. He said he didn't want me to wait till Monday to get it and I'm glad because I sure would hate to have to wait over Sunday for it.

I hope I didn't make you feel bad in my last letter about you not writing so much, but Honey, all I've got to look forward to is your letters. They are all that keeps me going. I love you so much and when I don't hear from you before the week is up, I get so nervous. I can't stand it. I can't do my work right or anything.

You said to think of you at night. Honey, you are on my mind all the time. I can't think of anything else. Everywhere I go and every minute of the day I think of you. I dream of you most every night. I go to bed and I roll and toss and fight myself to go to sleep. You can't imagine how terrible it is. I know I just couldn't go on without you.

I'm making out OK. I do hope you are feeling better now after you have got rested up. I know you were run down and I hope you won't lose more weight. You said you looked terrible with your eyes swelled without sleep, but you would look good to me.......

I'll bet Abbey Park did bring back memories, Hon. I would have liked to be there with you. I'm sure I will never forget it. The only part I hated was having to leave to catch the truck back to camp. I wish I could go for a walk down the streets with you again. If it was possible, I would pay off the money I owe Mrs. Lewis for the materials for the house and I'd get the rest somehow and come over as fast as I can.

It's nice that Joyce is helping you out. I sent you your parcel, but I couldn't get both cans of Crisco in it, so I'll send another sometime this week with some other things. Let me know when you get it so I know how long it takes.

I'm having a hell of a time with the money. I can't seem to make it go far enough. I only paid $7.00 on my car loan as I just couldn't make this month come out right. I paid off all the old bills and I hope to get on the others. I have $10.00 for Mrs. Lewis and I'll pay her Monday.

I've read your last letter five times and I suppose I will read it another 20 or more times. Please write a lot next time, Honey, as I sure enjoy them and look forward to getting them. They are all that keeps me going. I also got a letter from your Mom. I'll answer it after noon. It was nice of her to write, but I like yours a lot better. I wish you could write to me every day, but I know that takes too much. So I guess I will have to be satisfied with what I get.

I've cut down on smoking, my sweet. I bought a carton last Friday a week ago and I still have two packs left. I wish I could quit entirely. I hope you don't take it up since you are where you can get the weak brands.

I haven't done anything on the house, Honey, I can't seem to get in the mood. I want to have it finished for you. Well, Hon, I'm running out of paper. I've got lots more I want to say, but no room to put it. I love you, dearest, so much and I'm going to love you to death when you get here, believe me.

So till the next time I'll say so long. As ever, just Henry, your ever loving husband.

P.S. Have you been to any dances? Please be careful, Hon, as I don't trust some men and you know they can't be trusted. You are always worth a second look and some of them get ideas, so please be careful. You know I am jealous as can be and would fight any man who touches you. I'm sorry, I know I can't say that I don't want you to go dancing, but you know what is right and wrong. Just be careful.

Dorothy's response:

Henry don't worry so much about me. I haven't touched a cigarette and I don't intend to. I haven't been to any dances, just the cinema once. I hope you get started on the house. Honey, I will be very disappointed if you don't finish it. I can already picture what it will be like when I get there.

Am I doing better at writing? Paula's boyfriend, Karl, has bought a new motorbike and he's going to take me for a ride on it. I always did like to ride on one. Well, my dearest, here's my love. Write soon. I love you so much. Bye Bye, Dorothy XXXXXX

From Dorothy:

My dearest sweetheart, your wonderful letter came this noon. It was a week and a day since your last letter and I've been so worried. I've haunted the mail box time and time again and each time I was disappointed. My heart sank, please my darling, don't wait a week to write. I asked you in my last letter if you would write twice a week. If you do, as soon as I get them, I'll answer right away so you will get two each week also. Gosh, Honey, your letters mean so much to me. I worry everyone here asking if there is any mail for me. Honey, are you feeling alright? When you say you are going downhill fast, I wonder if you are sick. When I read that, I wept bitterly. Honey, if anything happened to you, I'd die instead. Life would be meaningless without you. I love you with everything that's in me. Please, please, my darling, don't worry about me. I will be with you soon, where I belong. I want you to go out and do things and take your mind off of us. Let people talk, I wouldn't believe them, you know that. I hope you say in your next letter that you feel better.

Uncle Lawrence took me and my cousin, Malcom to Bradgate Park on Wednesday. We went by bus and then walked up to the Old John lookout past the ruins. My goodness, I was puffed out by the time I got there. We took some sandwiches and Uncle Lawrence bought some cakes and a pot of tea. We did enjoy it. I was invited to Joyce's house for tea this week and it was a nice bus ride also to Narboro Road. My friend, Nellie Upton, who lives up past the dog stadium, had me come up. We had a nice talk and I met her new husband. I think getting out and doing a little visiting has done me some good. I have only been to the cinema once and a ride on a motorbike with a friend. Well, my precious, I'll close for now. Write soon, I love you, darling. XXXX Fondest love, Dorothy.

Dorothy continued to write newsy letters expressing her love to Henry just as he wanted and as she had promised. She knew that he missed her and she felt the same. It was just hard to express it properly in a letter.

From Dorothy:

Hello my Dearest, I received another letter from you today. My, was I surprised and happy. A letter does so much for you, doesn't it? I do hope it's helping you to feel better. I can't think of anything else I'd rather do. Last night Mam and I went up to sit with Grandmother Wade. She is very sick, in fact, the doctor said she may go at any time. I had to leave your letter last night, honey, as Da told me Mam wanted me to meet her at Gran's. It was quite late when we got home. I haven't had a minute to spare today, washing and ironing.

I know we will soon be together. Oh, honey I do miss you so much. You're so much a part of me. Gosh, but how I love you. You are my first waking thought and last at night. Whenever I go upstairs I kiss you in our wedding picture. It is on the dressing table. You look so dear, honey. I wish it was really you. I can't seem to express myself properly as to what you mean to me, but what I do say comes from the heart.

Thank your Mam for me for looking after you so good. You know when I get there we are going to live on love, is that alright with you?

From Henry:

My sweetest, I am trying to get the house done for you. The double door looks good and I know you will be proud of it. I plan to paper the kitchen since it is small and won't take much. Honey, the house is in a hell of a mess, I don't know where to turn. The power saw is in the front room and everything is dirty as can be and I've got stuff all over the kitchen. But don't worry, I'll have it all looking swell when you get here.

I wish I could be with you. I know I'm a fool, a poor fool, but I don't have the spirit to go ahead with anything. Everything seems to back fire in my face. Oh, Honey, I love you so much, I'm blind to everything else. We were meant for each other because I know I could never love or do anything with any other woman like I could do for you. You are a part of me and without you I feel like I've been cut in two. I need you, my other half, to operate. We will have many happy years together and I'll forget the time I have spent without you.

I do hope you can get a ship coming this way any time, the sooner the better for me as I need you to help me along. But I need the time to fix the house and prepare for your coming. I figure it will take me three more weeks to get it the way I want it.

Tell me sweet, do you want to live in England and make it your home or would you rather have me and Iowa? Please tell me. You are so important to me. I can't stop telling you how much I love you. I could go on forever writing it to you. Do you remember that song, 'until I waltz again with you?' They played it several times at the Legion Hall and I couldn't think to play cards for thinking about waltzing again with you even if I would step on your feet. I hope you would forgive me.

I'd better close for now, Honey. I'll try to write again Saturday night and get it off Sunday morning. Til then I love you, sweet thing. As ever, Henry.

Dorothy had thought of those last few letters during the long ocean crossing on the **SS Argentina**. The thousand-mile train ride from New York to Iowa seemed even longer and extremely uncomfortable and tiring. Seventeen hours on the train were excruciating. It was impossible to sleep sitting upright in those hard straight-backed seats. The train was full and the rumble of people talking and children crying filled the day and into the night. Henry didn't want to sleep much for fear a stranger might try to take Dorothy's belongings. He was determined to be alert to protect her.

"Henry, you need to get some sleep. Lean on me and close your eyes for at least a short while. I'll watch the bags and wake you if I need help." Dorothy pleaded with him the next morning.

"Well, just for a moment or two." He said as he lowered his head and began snoring straight away.

Dorothy was alone with her thoughts and the memory of her Da snoring across the hall seemed a long time ago even though it had only been a few weeks. She wondered what Mam and the girls were doing. 'Had Jack and Dorothy had the baby they were expecting? Would she ever get to meet her little niece or nephew? Had Joyce and Ray set a date for their wedding yet? Were Cath and Barney still happily married? Was Paula still dating Karl? Was Victoria up to her usual orneriness?' The thoughts flooded through her head and the tears quietly slid down her face. She wiped them away quickly, she didn't want to wake Henry and have him see her crying. He would be so disappointed if he knew how homesick she was beginning to feel already. She knew his rest was much needed, as much as hers had been, so she wiped away her tears and tried to focus on her new life ahead.

The train rumbled along and Henry woke after a brief nap feeling much better. "Hello, my sweet little wife." Dorothy leaned in for a kiss and smiled to herself that all her worrying about him had been in vain. He still loved her and wanted to spend the rest of their lives together. Little hardships along the way would probably be unavoidable, but their love would see them through anything, she was sure. She was looking forward, although a bit tentatively, to meeting her new family and seeing the house that Henry had lovingly built for them. She knew in her heart that life in America was going to be beautiful.

When Dorothy arrived in Iowa in March of 1946, the local newspaper ran their wedding picture with a caption. **Iowa Has Bundle from Britain Who Finds Us Friendly and Easy to Get on With.** It further stated that she preferred Iowa to New York City but felt the snow didn't intrigue her. "It's a bit deep" was her comment. She had left England on February 19, 1946 and "found the ocean journey not too bad, but it wasn't much fun to leave my parents and brothers and sisters." She immediately flashed a broad smile and said, "But, I think I shall like America very much".

During the long months they were apart after they were married, Henry had missed her so much that he wanted to know about her every day-to-day activity no matter how mundane. His letters were full of requests for more information. Henry wanted her to get to Iowa as soon as she could and the waiting was driving him crazy. He expressed his anger about her not applying for her entry permit sooner. Dorothy was not happy to get that letter.

From Dorothy:

Hello my Darling. First thing, I want to tell you; <u>I've got my entry permit</u>. I wanted to tell you as soon as I got it because I had said I would have to make a trip to London, but didn't need to. They said it could be sent to the Birmingham office, but then I got a reply today and they sent it through the mail here, so I don't have to go anywhere. Isn't that wonderful? I felt so good inside, it means my getting to you is certain.

About the last letter you wrote. I really don't know what to think about it. I honestly, can't see where I deserved it. You never even waited to see if anything would come through. I said I had to make inquiries. I'll tell you one thing, if you hoped you'd make me feel bad, you succeeded. You sounded like you blamed me for it all when I've done my best for you. Please don't ever write another letter like that, I burnt it in the fireplace where it belonged.

So, it seems that not all were words of love and passion. But Dorothy did later forgive him and continued to write newsy letters, just with not as much talk of her love. It took her a while to express it again. She shared about her day-to-day happenings, but refrained from expressing much more. It was hard to forgive and forget when Henry was so far away. His angry letter gave her a bit of a pause about his temper and whether their married life would be as smooth as she had first imagined. She kept those thoughts to herself and had shared only her day-to-day happenings.

From Dorothy:

My Dearest. Well, I went up and sat with Gran for two hours yesterday. She is very ill and she is so afraid of being by herself and dying with no one with her. Mam is sleeping with her at night because it makes her feel better. The doctor says it's a miracle how she's lived this long.

Geoffrey and Dottie moved into their new home last week near Wigston. He has invited us up on Sunday. It takes two buses so it will be a nice ride.

I'm glad to hear you got your tax return. It will get the worry of the cost of the house off your mind. I'll be there soon and we will pay the bills together.

I realize how you felt when you wrote that letter, and my sweet, I never thought you would miss me so much, but it doesn't help to take it out on me, does it? I love you so much and we will be together soon. Bye Bye, your loving wife.

The long days of waiting and the letter writing was over and Dorothy and Henry's life in Iowa was to begin.

Chapter Twenty-Four

When Dorothy at last arrived in Iowa, she loved the little house the moment she saw it. "Oh, Henry, it's beautiful. I knew it would be. You did this just for me?" she said as she wrapped her arms around his neck. She thought the little white house with the red roof was perfect. She hadn't known they actually made red roofing shingles. There was no such thing in England, but she was glad that Henry had chosen them. They reminded her of the red brick of the Council houses and it made her feel right at home.

There hadn't been much money after the war ended. Momma Collins had saved some from the Army pay he had sent, so when he returned from overseas, he borrowed $1,000 from Mrs. Lewis, a friend of their family. There was just enough to buy the land and the materials he needed to build the house himself. It would take Dorothy and Henry several years to pay back that borrowed money, but the payments were their first priority and were always faithfully delivered in cash to Mrs. Lewis. The pride of owning their home free and clear meant the world to them.

There wasn't a lot of money for anyone after the war ended and even though $1,000 doesn't sound like very much, in 1946 it was a fortune. To make the money stretch as far as possible, Henry built the house with his own two hands. Architects, carpenters and other construction workers were never part of the plan. There were no drawings, just an image in his mind of how it would look. It took him many months working evenings after long days at his job. Both were physical work and the evenings and weekends were tiring, but his love of working with his hands, building the home for his young bride kept him plugging away. He had moments of loneliness that delayed progress and he had written to Dorothy about it. His good friend, Fred Carter lived just down the road and he came by to boost Henry's spirits and helped out whenever he could. Other family members stopped in on weekends to help dig the basement and nail a board or two. It was back breaking work, but it was done with love and anticipation. Since the money was limited, when it was finished, it was a small square "box" with a tiny front porch, a back porch, and that long back yard that ended at the weeds hiding the railroad tracks.

The house consisted of only four small rooms: the living room, kitchen and two bedrooms with a tiny bathroom in between. The only "inside" doors were the two in the bathroom separating it from the kitchen and the back bedroom. Otherwise, a doorway between the two bedrooms was open to each. The back bedroom looked over the long back yard and held a double sized bed and one chest of drawers. From the back bedroom there was an open doorway that led to the bedroom at the front of the house which Dorothy and Henry shared. From there the front bedroom was open to the living room. It was kind of like what people would call "open concept" today on home décor and designer channels. Henry had built the bedroom/living room door extra wide with open shelves on either side where Dorothy displayed her favorite knickknacks. It was not an ideal situation for privacy but Henry knew Dorothy would love it.

And she did. Decorating and cleaning it was very important to her. The floors were hardwood with woodwork that matched. Henry had sanded, stained, and varnished them and Dorothy would scrub and wax the floors to such a brilliant shine that you could see your reflection. With one reminder: be careful of slipping on an area rug.

Dorothy especially loved their sunny and bright bedroom that was on the northeast side of the house. The sun would rise in the morning, flooding the room with beautiful golden rays. She had decorated the room with matching curtains and bedspread with tiny pink flowers on them. There were lace sheers behind the curtains and fluffy throw pillows on top of the bedspread. It was a little feminine for Henry's tastes, but he knew that Dorothy loved it so he never objected. During spring cleaning Dorothy would wash those sheers and stretch the fabric onto the little nails of the curtain stretcher in the back yard where they would dry before they were hung again at the two light filled windows. One never forgets the smell of freshly washed lace as it dries in the sun, nor the pain of the prick on the finger from the little nails. Heaven forbid if you bled on the curtain so that it had to be washed again!

Each and every morning, Dorothy made the bed and never was anyone allowed to sit on the bed once the bedspread was on. Having her very own home was a wonder and a treasure to Dorothy and she worked at keeping it immaculate, so a rumpled bedspread would not do.

Yes, some would call Dorothy a "clean freak". She was very organized and diligent in her regular routine. Monday was washday, Tuesday ironing, Wednesday sweeping and dusting, Thursday scrubbing the floors, Friday bath time and bathroom cleanup. Saturdays were for grocery shopping and Sunday for church. She lived by the old adage a place for everything and everything in its place. She would say, "If your bed is made, the dishes done, and things put in their proper place, then your home will look clean even if it isn't ready for the white glove test". She had settled nicely into her new home in America.

Henry had smiled when Dorothy had exclaimed her love for the house the moment she saw it. "I'm so glad. I had a hard time concentrating on the project with you still in England and me here. I wasn't sure I could do it at first. Mom and dad encouraged me and Fred was a big help. I wouldn't have finished it without his encouragement and my family. I know it's not much, but it is ours."

"Oh, my, Henry, I never imagined I would ever have my own house and never anything as splendid as this. You are amazing," Dorothy exclaimed as she hugged and kissed him with all the passion she had been holding back for so long. Henry was eager to share his passion as well. That night in the comfort of her new home in her very own bed, she came to truly know her husband. The first time on their honeymoon in London seemed so long ago. But, in the weeks to come, she learned that Henry had a passion that surpassed her own. Mam had always talked about how Da liked his pleasures and expected her to do her "wifely duties", as she called it. Dorothy came to feel like Henry could be a bit like her Da in that respect. She tried to shake off the feelings but it was always in the back of her mind when they went to bed. Her mother's warnings of the wifely duties played on her. She soon felt a bit reluctant when Henry began snuggling close each night. She knew what he wanted so she began prolonging her bedtime preparations until she heard him snoring softly in the bedroom. When Henry mentioned it at breakfast one morning, she knew that their differences were to become a problem.

Bertha Collins had a pleasant face and would whistle as she worked so she and Dorothy got along well. Bertha reminded Dorothy of her own mother and she quickly came to love her in spite of missing her own Mam. But talking to her about intimate things was not something Dorothy could do. So Dorothy kept her feelings about their sexual problems to herself and hoped that Henry's amorous ways would settle down in time.

His passion had been strong during those first few months and Dorothy struggled to keep up her wifely duties with joy. She truly loved him, but knew that her physical desires would never be the same as his. When she complained of a stomachache for several days, Henry insisted that she go see old Doc Smith. She was surprised when he came into the examination room after she had dressed and heard him say, "Dorothy, I'm pleased to tell you that you are pregnant. And by February of next year you will have a new baby in your home."

When she burst into tears, old Doc Smith gave her a gentle hug and said, "There, there Dorothy, there's nothing to cry about. You are young and in good health, so you will have a strong healthy baby." She didn't know whether the tears were tears of joy or terror. 'Oh my,' Dorothy thought to herself. 'What will Henry think?' She knew they had talked about having children, but she was sure that he hadn't meant so soon.

As she sat in the doctor's exam room, Dorothy thought about how she was going to tell him. In the comfort of her new home, her very own house, she had immersed herself into her wifely duties but not without some hesitation. Henry had been gentle and kind, but he also had a man's appetite. At first she had been thrilled at the attention and love that he showered on her, but she felt certain that she did not share the same level of passion for the marital bed. She was scared but thrilled at the news of a baby to love and care for. Besides, maybe that would mean Henry would not be so amorous for a while, but how was she going to tell him that there were now consequences of his regular sexual advances.

Dorothy herself didn't know if she was ready to be a mother. She didn't know anything about having babies and she didn't want to talk to Momma Collins about it. Her own mother hadn't been much help in that department either. Dorothy knew that in between Paula and Victoria there had been two miscarriages. But it had not been something they had discussed. Ellen had said that Da had been an aggressive husband who demanded she do her wifely duties, but that was the extent of information from Mam. Dorothy knew how babies were conceived but just what to do while expecting them was frightening. She knew she would have to approach the subject with Momma Collins after all.

Bertha had laughed and said, "I knew my Henry would get right to it. That's wonderful, honey."

"But Momma Collins, I don't know anything about babies and I feel sick every morning and don't feel like doing my housework."

"Oh, don't worry about that, it'll pass. Everyone gets morning sickness. I had it with all seven of my pregnancies."

"No, Momma Collins, I don't like it and I certainly don't want seven pregnancies," as Dorothy slumped in a chair and began to cry.

"Honey, you will be fine. I'm here and I'll help you through it. What did Henry say?"

"I haven't told him yet. Do you think he'll be mad?"

"Mad? Why should he be mad? Henry has talked about having kids since he was one himself. You'll see."

Dorothy wasn't sure but later that night after supper, "Henry, I have some news," Dorothy began hesitantly. She knew they didn't have much money. They were still making payments to Mrs. Lewis for the house, so the news of a baby on the way might be a little disturbing.

Her fears quickly vanished when Henry picked her up and swung her around, "Oh, Dorothy, that's wonderful. I hope we have lots of babies." Dorothy smiled back with a bit of uneasiness on her face. Lots of babies were not what she really had in mind. One or two would be sufficient.

The first few months of the pregnancy were not at all what Dorothy had anticipated when she first learned about the coming baby. The days went by slowly and Dorothy suffered from the morning sickness that lasted long after morning. When Henry came home from work, he would grieve at the gaunt look on his beautiful wife's face. "Were you sick again today, honey? I wish there was something I could do."

"Momma Collins has helped. She mixed up some concoction and made me drink it. It tasted awful, but I do feel a bit better." Dorothy said as she put her head on Henry's shoulder. He was always so good to comfort her in spite of the long day he put in at work, so she tried to have supper ready to put on the table when he arrived. He would lie down on the living room couch for a short nap while she put the finishing touches on the meal. He reminded her of Da and his **Daily Mirror** in the old thread bare green chair where he would fall asleep in front of the fireplace after he had his stomach full. Those memories would pop into her head at the oddest moments and they always made her feel homesick for Mam and their brick Council house on Burfield Street. Even though it had only been a few months, it seemed like ages ago that she had put her bag into Uncle Lawrence's car and left her old life behind at the Leicester Rail Station.

The pregnancy went better after the first few months. She and Henry shopped for a few things and the family provided some worn but still very usable baby items. Momma Collins gave them a beautiful new baby carriage or pram, as Dorothy called it. Dorothy knew Momma Collins must have scrimped on her household money for months to be able to purchase it. Bertha beamed as Dorothy hugged her with true feelings and Dorothy felt a bit more at home now that she had a substitute Mam to love her. Momma Collins had been so understanding about Dorothy's inexperience and fear at being pregnant.

Henry built a beautiful crib and Dorothy marveled at his abilities. He truly had a gift for working with his hands and wood. He had applied a beautiful stain and then a shiny varnish finish. Dorothy purchased a soft yellow coverlet to put over the mattress. Barbara Jean Collins was born on February 22, 1947 and brought home to their little house with the red roof. She was a pretty baby with soft blonde hair, striking blue eyes like Henry's and the fair English complexion like her mother's.

In spite of their happiness at having their first daughter and the prettiness of the baby, Barbara proved to be quite difficult. She was a colicky baby and cried a lot. Dorothy nursed the baby at regular intervals as she had been told, just as Mam had done with all her babies, but Barbara never seemed to be satisfied. Within a few minutes after feeding, she would begin to cry again. She seemed to have her days and nights mixed up and many long hours were spent holding her and rocking her until they both fell asleep from exhaustion. Dorothy caught as many cat naps as she could while the baby was sleeping, but it didn't do Henry much good to hear the baby crying all night. He spent many a long hard day at work with very little rest.

Finally, in exasperation Dorothy went to see old Doc Smith. He had delivered hundreds of babies and Momma Collins said he would know what to do. Dorothy shared the information about all the home remedies that Momma Collins had offered and how the efforts had been to no avail. Doc checked the baby over and said she was in good health, but suggested switching to a prepared formula. "Maybe she's just hungry. If she's not getting enough to eat, she'll cry. Maybe your milk doesn't have as much nutrient as she needs or it upsets her stomach. You did spend a lot of years not eating the proper foods during the war in Europe." Taking his advice, Dorothy changed Barbara to a bottle of formula and peace came to the Collins household. At least with regard to the baby.

Chapter Twenty-Five

Dorothy didn't know how she would have managed if it had not been for Momma Collins. She had accepted Dorothy into her family with love and patience, although Bertha Collins's own fears were realized when she discovered that Dorothy was indeed green at being a wife. Dorothy took to keeping her house clean right away because she loved having her very own house. Keeping track of the money and household items was not a problem either. She even adjusted to caring for the baby right away. A mother's instinct always kicks in. But cooking was another matter!

Shortly after she had arrived, Dorothy had asked, "Momma Collins, will you help me to learn how to cook Henry's favorite things? I'm sorry I'm not a proper wife taking care of her husband, but Mam never taught me how to cook because of the war rations. With things so scarce, she couldn't afford to waste anything. I know a few things about English dishes and Henry says he's just a meat, potato and gravy kind of guy. But he wants homemade bread and pies. I don't know anything about making them. He works so hard every day at the garage and I want to feed him what he wants. I've never made a roast with gravy, bread or a pie or anything, and he says he doesn't like vegetables, so I don't know why he let me plant that big garden at the back of the yard." It all spilled out in one big breath as Dorothy started to cry.

Bertha Collins smiled, "Don't worry yourself, Honey. He let you plant the garden because you said you wanted to eat fresh vegetables that you never had in England during the war. He doesn't mind if you grow them and cook them, just don't insist that he eat them. I'll tell you everything you need to know. Come on now, dry your tears and let's get started." Momma Collins was more than happy to teach Dorothy a few things in the kitchen.

She told Dorothy that Henry was not a picky eater. Even though he didn't care a lot about vegetables, meat, potatoes and gravy would always make him happy. The best way for him to finish off a meal was to dip a slice of homemade bread into the remaining gravy and sop his plate, or to have a big slice of pie. He did like fresh fruit pies even if he didn't want any vegetables.

'How in the world did a person make a loaf of bread or a pie? Mam has always gone to the bakery around the corner before the war', Dorothy thought in a panic. Mam had made scones and toad-in-the-hole regularly because they were Da's favorite. Dorothy loved them too, but had never learned how to make them herself.

"Dorothy, there are just a few simple things you need to learn about feeding Henry. Always have plenty of gravy. You don't have to spend a lot of money on fancy cuts of meat. An inexpensive roast will make good gravy. Put a few potatoes around it to bake in the oven and make gravy from the meat drippings when it's done and he'll be happy. Have some good bread for him to dip and he'll never complain. I'll teach you later how to bake bread and a pie, but for now just get the basics of what you need at the grocery store. Mostly, all you need to do is have the food ready to put on the table when he gets home from work. He'll be patient with you learning, I know it."

Dorothy knew she could at least have the meals ready when Henry got home. Not a problem. Mam had taught her that having the food on the table was the way to keep a man happy, that, and the wifely duties. Dorothy knew she could manage the wifely duties when she had to, but cooking was something she struggled with. So far it had been oatmeal, bologna sandwiches, and canned soup. Henry hadn't complained, but Dorothy knew he was tired of that menu. So Dorothy listened to Momma Collins and set out to make her first real Sunday dinner.

But in spite of Bertha's instructions, Dorothy's first attempt at a roast was not a success. She thought she was following everything Momma Collins had told her. But she had put the potatoes around the roast without peeling them or cutting them into small pieces. That wouldn't have been so bad if she hadn't ruined everything else as well. The potatoes were burnt around the edges and still hard in the middle. She had put them in too late and by the time she thought they were done, the roast was dry and shriveled up. She hadn't put enough water in the pan for everything to cook properly. She attempted to make gravy, but it was lumpy and not much of it. Henry didn't have enough to dip his bread into. Dorothy thought that even though Momma Collins had shared information, the specific instructions had been a bit vague and Dorothy didn't know how to improvise. Consequently, her first real Sunday dinner was a disaster.

"Honey, it's alright," Henry comforted his tearful wife. "Don't give up, you will learn."

"But Henry," Dorothy sniffled. "I wanted my first Sunday roast to be perfect. I thought I followed Momma Collins' directions, but I guess not. And I don't even know how to make Yorkshire pudding like Mam always made. It's not Sunday dinner if we don't have a Yorkshire." Dorothy sniffled more as the tears ran down her face.

Henry gave his wife a hug and wiped her tears. He sat down at the table and ate every bit of the food she had prepared even though it was almost inedible. He hoped that with a little more time Dorothy would learn from Momma Collins. Otherwise, he was going to starve to death! He wasn't sure he could handle any more oatmeal, bologna sandwiches and soup. He shuddered at the thought of her attempting to bake bread and pies. He feared she would burn down the house!

Dorothy wrote to Mam about her disastrous attempt at preparing a Sunday dinner. Mam wrote back detailed instructions on how to make a Yorkshire pudding and some of the other things Dorothy had grown up eating. Henry soon learned to enjoy English cooking as well as the things that Momma Collins taught Dorothy and his fear of starvation soon disappeared.

Henry had taken a job at a local garage working on cars. The owner, Mr. Floyd was a good family friend and had offered Henry the position when he had learned about the new bride coming from England. He had known Henry since he was a boy and knew that he had always been a good family man, even leaving school so young to help at home. Working on the railroad had not been available when Henry returned from the war and jobs were hard to find. Henry found odd jobs and work wherever he could. Mr. Floyd knew that Henry was a hard worker and willing to learn. He needed some help in his garage as his car dealership was also growing a bit and he could use an extra hand in getting things done. He knew he would have a good employee in Henry.

The days at the garage were long and Henry came home tired and dirty. Dorothy shuddered at the greasy grimy clothes she had to wash and the grease and oil from the cars smelled awful. It had been particularly distasteful when she had been expecting the baby. Da had never gotten that dirty in his gardens. But Momma Collins was there to help with the wash and taught Dorothy how to use the old wringer washer and showed her the best way to hang the clothes properly on the line in the back yard to dry in the warm summer sunshine. The long winter months were much more difficult with having to hang clothes to dry in the house. Keeping the diapers washed and dried was a never-ending task. Dorothy did miss the mild weather in England. The snow and ice of Iowa was something she could have never imagined. And Iowa's weather was just part of the things that were and different and disturbing for Dorothy.

Although Dorothy loved Henry and was thrilled about little Barbara's arrival, she couldn't get the feeling of loneliness and homesickness out of her heart. She missed Mam so much. They had always been so close. Many a night after her job at the dog track, they would sit in the kitchen over a cup of tea and toast, share their day's happenings, and talk about their hopes and dreams for Dorothy's future. Mam had wanted to see Dorothy happily married with children, but she certainly hadn't imagined her finding her happiness in America!

Dorothy had always known that Mam was not happy in her marriage and that Jack Parnell was a difficult man to live with. So when Dorothy told Mam she was going to marry Henry and move to America, Ellen was apprehensive. She couldn't bear the thought of her precious daughter leaving. She had worried that Henry might turn out to be just like Jack. 'How can I comfort her if she is thousands of miles away?' was constantly on Ellen's mind. During their long talks after Dorothy and Henry were married and Henry had returned to America after the war, Ellen had shared about her own husband's infidelity and mean nature and her fears for Dorothy's future. Dorothy assured her Mam that Henry would not be like Da.

Months later after Dorothy had arrived in Iowa, Ellen faithfully kept her promises to write letters each week. Even though those letters were filled with news of home, they could never quite fill the void they both felt and Dorothy would read them over and over. Often she would retreat to the back bedroom of their little house, emerging from the bedroom with red eyes and a sniffling nose. Even though Momma and Papa Collins were dears and the rest of family had eventually accepted her, it just wasn't the same as her home in England. The pain of homesickness began to grow stronger. She struggled to hide it from Henry.

When Dorothy had written to Mam about the coming baby, she knew that Mam would be happy for her. Ellen was happy for her daughter, of course, but also had some misgivings about Dorothy's readiness to handle it along with all the other adjustments she was making to her new life in America. 'Oh, how I wish I could be with her.'

Dorothy was frugal with her housekeeping money just as Mam had been. Unlike Jack Parnell, Henry brought his pay envelope home faithfully every week and gave it to Dorothy to manage. Dorothy would immediately separate it into other envelopes. There was one envelope to pay annual bills, one for monthly bills, and one for weekly groceries and other expenses.

The most important envelope though, was the savings one. Henry had promised Dorothy that she could return to England for a visit whenever they could save enough money. So Dorothy was diligent in putting every spare penny away in that special envelope.

In the early years, they didn't have a bank account, so Dorothy kept the cash in the envelopes and hid them under some boxes on the top shelf of the bathroom cupboard. She felt they would be safe in the tall cupboard at the end of the bathtub. So, whenever money was needed Dorothy would climb up and reach in to retrieve the proper envelope. Even as she grew bigger with the baby, the climb to the top of the cupboard was a weekly ritual.

If Henry had known about the climbing, he probably would have insisted immediately that they get a bank account. Fortunately, no mishaps occurred and Dorothy was glad he hadn't found out about her climbing because she liked having her money envelopes close by. She liked seeing the money grow and to proudly take out enough to pay the bills each month. Her meager earnings in England had been handled the same, some for Mam, some for bills, and some for savings. She was thrilled that Henry believed the husband made the money and the woman of the house should know how to take care of it. That was so different from her parents' lives. She wished Da had been more like Henry and maybe life would have been easier for Mam.

The weekly, monthly and annual envelopes grew and shrank as their contents were needed. There were always groceries to purchase. The light bill and the water and heating bills had to be paid monthly. And, of course, there was the money to Mrs. Lewis to repay her for the help she had given Henry to build their lovely little home.

Throughout it all, the savings envelope continued to grow as well, but more slowly than Dorothy would have liked. The promise of a trip back to England was foremost in Dorothy's mind and she put away as much as possible each pay period, often depriving herself and the family of other things she felt were too frivolous. Her letters to Mam each week told of her growing savings envelope. She didn't know how soon she was going to be able to make the trip though; it was so costly.

Ellen's letters to her daughter were full of daily information about the family. Geoffrey and Dottie had their first baby, Angela, before Dorothy left and she was growing like a weed. Their second daughter, Peg, followed soon after Angela. Their youngest, Jean, was born just a few months after Dorothy's own first child. Dorothy was sad that the Parnell family was changing without her around to share in it.

Allan, Dorothy's next older brother, and his wife, Olivia, had no children. It wasn't that they didn't want any, it just wasn't to be as soon as they had wanted. It would be many years later before their first son was born. Joyce and Ray were happily married and expecting their first baby, much to Allan and Olivia's sorrow. They were happy for Joyce, just disappointed they didn't have the same news. Their jealousy soon became a wedge between brother and sister and they didn't see each other as often as they had in the past. Finally, they severed contact altogether. When Dorothy learned of this, her concern for her family made it even harder to be so far away.

Paula and her beau, Karl, had decided their relationship wasn't working for them any longer. Mam said Paula was devastated, but held her head high and said she would find someone else. Victoria was doing well in school but might have to leave school if there was not enough money to allow her to go on for the next levels. Ellen wanted her youngest daughter to continue her education, but Ellen too was saving her money to possibly make a trip to America or to send the money to Dorothy to add to her savings.

The letters went on and on about the family and their daily lives in England. They meant so much to Dorothy, but also made her long for her far away home all the more. Her letters to Mam shared information about her daily living in Iowa. Dorothy told her mother about their lovely little home, Henry's job, Momma and Papa Collins, and of course, the baby.

Ellen longed to see her daughter so she continued to save every spare shilling she had. As Dorothy wrote her weekly letters, she didn't know that her life was about to change very soon in spite of not being able to plan her own trip home.

Chapter Twenty-Six

In the Fall of 1950 a letter from Mam came with exciting news. She and Paula and Victoria were coming to America! Ellen had finally decided to leave Jack Parnell after years of tolerating his infidelity, stinginess, and indifference. She felt she could provide a better life for herself and her two youngest daughters away from him. She had worked outside of the home for years to subsidize his meager offerings and knew that she could do better on her own. Leaving England and immigrating to America to be with Dorothy was the answer. Now that the girls were old enough to make the long trip, but young enough to make the adjustment of a new life, Ellen applied to immigrate to the United States.

Ellen hadn't said anything to Dorothy about her plans to immigrate until she knew for sure that she could. When she heard the news, Dorothy was ecstatic to learn that Mam and the girls were coming. Oh, how she had longed for them for the past four years. She had been diligent in putting money in the savings envelope above the bathtub, but it had grown slowly and whenever she had mentioned making a trip, Henry was adamant that he didn't want her to go. When she learned that Mam planned to come to America, she was so excited she didn't give a second thought to what this might mean for Henry and her American family.

Dorothy set about making plans for Mam and the girls coming. She decided to send some of her savings to Ellen to help with expenses. They, of course, would live with them in their house, Dorothy decided. Eventually they might find a place of their own close by, but Dorothy wanted them near her. The little back bedroom would surely be large enough for Mam and the girls to share. She and Henry had been talking about getting a regular full-sized bed for Barbara. Now they would get it for Mam and the girls to sleep in and Barbara could remain in her crib for the time being. It could easily be moved to fit in the corner. Dorothy had it all clear in her mind that it would be lovely to have all her family together.

She had not given much thought as to how this would affect Henry and their marriage. The thought of them all being together was all Dorothy could think about. She tried to restrain herself from talking about it daily and although he didn't say much, she knew that Henry did not share her excitement. Particularly when she told him she had sent her savings to Mam to help with the trip.

"You did what? But that was our savings. You sent it to her without asking me?"

"You said I could go see my family when I'd saved enough money. And I thought it'd be just as good to use it to have them come here instead. What's the difference?"

"What's the difference? That was our money. How could you throw away our money like that!" Henry's voice was rising and Dorothy's did too.

"Throw away? I used it to bring my family here."

"They're not my family!" Henry got up and stomped towards the bedroom and Dorothy followed him.

"But, why is it different? I want to see my family and whether they come here or I go there, what does it matter how we use the money?"

"We could have used that money for a different car. I'm barely keeping the old one running. Why didn't you ask me?"

"I didn't think I had to. You've always let me run the household and pay the bills and save the money. You never said anything about the car. And you promised I could go visit Mam when I saved enough."

"Well, I didn't think you would send the money to her." Dorothy began to cry. "Henry, you sound like you hate Mam. What's come over you?" And for the first time since he had fallen in love with her, Henry wasn't affected by Dorothy's tears. He had other things on his mind.

"Well, for one thing you haven't been very romantic since Barbara was born. You know that's important to me."

"What does that have to do with her coming? Besides, you knew I wasn't as interested in sexual intimacy as you are." Dorothy was starting to get mad with the way the conversation was going. "Mam always warned me that men want it their way." Dorothy turned to walk away.

"See, that's what I'm saying. She put those ideas in your head. I've been patient, but you need to warm up a bit."

"Warm up a bit? What's that supposed to mean?"

"You know what I'm talking about. She's told you it's just a wifely duty. Now she's going to be living with us in this little house. How will we ever have some private time?" Dorothy didn't want to discuss it any further. Mam was coming and that's what was important to her. "We can talk about it later!" Dorothy said as she turned and walked away leaving Henry looking at her in disgust.

"Yeh, talk." Henry knew that life in the little house with the red roof was not going to be the same once Ellen and the girls were in it.

When early Summer of 1951 arrived and along with it a weary Ellen, Paula and Victoria, Henry realized he had been right even before they got to Iowa. The trip had been difficult. The ocean crossing was one of the worst things they had ever experienced. The weather had not been good. The girls had been excited at first about the train ride from Leicester, the villages and fields going by were such fun to watch. But the trip across the ocean was another matter. The storms at sea kept the ship heaving from side to side and there was nothing to see except endless water. Even the occasional walk along the deck and the fresh air and food didn't help prevent them from the seasickness. Patience and understanding had long left Ellen as the girls complained endlessly that they didn't feel good and questioned why they had to go to America. The excitement of seeing Dorothy and starting a new life was lost over the side of the ship somewhere.

Dorothy told Henry he was to meet them in New York for the train trip to Iowa just as he had with her. He hadn't really wanted to go but Dorothy insisted that they could not make the trip alone. A middle-aged woman and two young girls would not be safe traveling that far. "Well, they managed to make it to Southampton alone and all the way across the ocean." Henry grumbled. He didn't relish the thought of the long train ride from New York to Iowa with Ellen and the girls chattering all the way.

"I know, Henry, but they will need you there after they process through Ellis Island and into the United States," Dorothy said with encouragement. "I remember how hard it was for me. I couldn't have done it without Gertrude. Please, please, don't make it worse. You know how much Mam means to me. Having her come here is a dream come true. Don't spoil it for me. I've missed them all so much. We will be just one big happy family, you'll see."

Henry never doubted they would be one big family, happy was another matter.

"Yes, but letting them live with us, how will we all manage in this small house? Can't we help find them a place of their own? They can live close by, this isn't a large town like Leicester, you know. They wouldn't be far away."

"And just how are they to pay for a place of their own? Mam will need to find a job, of course, but she won't find one right away. Are there even any places to rent in town?" Dorothy asked with tears in her eyes. Henry rejecting the idea of her family living with them had not occurred to her. She was so excited to have them coming. She hadn't really thought about the logistics of it all. She knew Mam wouldn't mind that they were going to have to share the one bedroom, they had done it before. Dorothy remembered how she and her three sisters had shared a single room in one double bed their entire lives before she married Henry, so she knew Mam and the girls would make do as well.

Dorothy gave little thought that her childhood room had been upstairs and there had been a door to close. Here in their little house there were no doors to close between the rooms and the distance was less than ten feet from their bed to where Ellen and the girls would sleep. When Dorothy did let herself think about it, she had to admit she had some apprehension about how it all would work. She knew that Henry would still want them to be intimate.

'Oh, dear', she thought to herself. 'It will be an adjustment. But, we will manage, after all, we are family.'

Momma and Papa Collins were surprised when they learned the news. They shared Henry's concern about all of them living under the same roof in that little house. 'Why, there was only the one small bathroom. How are three adults and three children supposed to share that?' In spite of their misgivings, not wanting to upset Dorothy, Momma and Papa Collins kept quiet about their own concerns. Except Momma Collins did offer one bit of advice and cautioned Dorothy about curbing her enthusiasm around Henry. "He will need time to adjust," she had said. Dorothy didn't think about Henry's need to adjust; her only focus was on Mam's coming to be with her!

The day of their arrival could not come soon enough for Dorothy. Letters had been exchanged for several months filled with the plans. Anticipation was high on both sides of the Atlantic Ocean. When the time finally came, Dorothy hope that the crossing was mild and none of them had been seasick. She had shared the information she had been given by her Porter about how to avoid the problem. She told Mam to partake of the fresh air and good food. Paula and Victoria were excited to be coming, Ellen had written. Although Paula was concerned about leaving her boyfriend, Karl. They had been dating when Dorothy left, but then had broken up soon afterwards. In one of Mam's recent letters she had mentioned that they were again seeing each other. Mam had said she was sure Paula would adjust nicely once they got to Iowa and would forget all about him. Karl wasn't the proper man for Paula anyway, she had added. Surely there were some nice young men nearby. Ellen had offered the idea in trying to reassure Paula. But Paula wasn't completely sold on the idea of America and meeting someone else. After all, Karl had begged her to stay with a promise of marriage.

When Henry arrived at the dock in New York, he recognized Ellen and the girls immediately even though Victoria was now almost fourteen and had grown tall and gangly. Paula was twenty-one and looked a lot the same, but rather sullen. Victoria saw Henry immediately and shouted, "Tom, Tom, we're over here." Henry laughed to himself about the name. He was going to have to teach them to use his real name. Even though he had told his family about the silly misunderstanding, he knew Momma Collins would not want him to be called "Tom", especially since there was actually a real Tom Collins in the family. Papa Collins's sister had had a child out of wedlock and so, of course, kept the family name of Collins for her son. Momma Collins did not want there to be any confusion about her son and his birth. Henry thought to himself, 'I'll have to get Ellen and the girls acclimated to America and my real name right away so Momma won't be upset.'

Henry took a deep breath and waved to them as Ellen and the girls dragged their luggage down the dock. He hurried to help them and they all walked to where there were taxies waiting to take them to the train station. In the cab, Victoria was excitedly chatting all the way about the crossing. She was glad to be off the ship and away from Ellis Island. "Tom, I mean, Henry, the boat was so big. There was so much food and our cabin was small, but I had the top bunk and Mam and Paula had the lower ones. We went up on deck every day, and the sea was so beautiful until it started to storm and we all got sick. I have never felt so awful." Victoria rambled along and Henry again wondered how it was going to work with all of them living in their small, four-room house.

Ellen's grumbling about having to board the train for another two days of travel did not help his disposition either. The train ride from New York to Iowa was going to be much longer than when he had picked up Dorothy. Of course, they had been so happy to see each other and just held each other close. There had been no need for them to talk much. Just being together again was all they needed. Now with the girls chattering incessantly and Ellen grumbling about the long trip, Henry thought the train was never going to get to Iowa. He sat in silence across the aisle staring out the window.

Seeing the look on his face, Ellen felt she should make an attempt to start a conversation. Perhaps she should talk about something other than the horrible trip. With a conviction she didn't really feel, she said, "Henry, it's nice of you to welcome us into your home. I hope we won't be too much trouble."

"It's what Dorothy wants, so we will make it work." Henry replied. Ellen picked up on his tone and wondered also how it was all going to work out if Henry didn't want them there. But she knew that if Dorothy wanted it that way, then it would be that way. Victoria chattered constantly to other people on the train. She seemed to make friends easily. Paula sulked in her seat alone. Henry and Ellen kept to themselves. There wasn't much more that either one of them wanted to say. The rest of the train ride passed slowly without incident or further conversation between them.

Dorothy had been pacing the floor and looking out the window for several days since Henry had left for New York. She was so anxious to see Mam again. The past four years had seemed so long. She had been saving her money each week to make a trip home, but it hadn't grown enough yet to afford for all three of them to go. Daily living expenses had to come first, so the savings envelope was not full enough. Sending some of it to Ellen had been the best thing to do in spite of Henry's anger when he found out. She still remembered how he had walked out the back door and let the screen door slam behind him. Dorothy, in her enthusiasm to be with her Mam again, hadn't considered Henry's opinion on the matter.

When their car did finally pull into the driveway, Dorothy ran out the door shouting, "Mam, oh, Mam", as she rushed into the open arms of her mother. They both had tears running down their faces as they hugged. Henry looked on with a mixture of emotions. He was happy to see Dorothy's joy, but he couldn't suppress his growing apprehension.

The girls had spilled out of the car first and looked around the yard, "Your own house, Dorothy, how wonderful, but it's nothing like our house! And you have grass and flowers in your front garden. Mam, Mam, are we really going to live here?" Victoria exclaimed in excitement. Even sulky Paula commented on how pretty it was. Ellen and Dorothy barely heard the girls as she and Mam clung to each other in their long embrace. "Mam, I've missed you so much. I can't believe you are here." Dorothy choked out the words.

"Dorothy you look happy, a bit thin, but happy. And where is my granddaughter?" Ellen asked before they were even in the house. "She's with Momma and Papa Collins." Dorothy told her. "I didn't want her to be scared with us crying and carrying on. She thinks she's a big girl for four and with a strong independent nature, but I didn't want to upset her if she saw me crying hysterically. I know she will love you as much as I do as soon as she gets to know you."

Henry carried their belongings into the house and Dorothy showed them the back bedroom they would be sharing. When Henry sat down their luggage and looked around the house now crowded with noisy people, he knew that things were not going to be the same for quite some time to come.

Dorothy was oblivious of Henry at that moment and the stressed look on his tired face. She was so caught up in the joy of having her family with her at last, she didn't notice as he slipped out the door quietly and walked down the street to Momma and Papa Collins' to fetch Barbara.

Dorothy really hadn't given much thought to the logistics of so many people living in their small house. She had convinced herself that it would all be wonderful. Bathroom usage soon proved to be hectic. It was planned that Henry would be allowed first in the mornings so he could be off to work. After that Dorothy would get herself and Barbara dressed for the day and then Ellen and the girls could take their turn. So, for the most part, it worked well, if not a bit of a shuffle. Evenings could be handled in reverse with everyone getting ready for bed.

Of course, intimacy with Henry, was a different matter. Dorothy had decided it was going to have to be limited. She knew that he would not be happy about that, but with no door between the bedrooms, she didn't want Mam and the girls to hear anything. Barbara was too young to know what the sounds she heard meant, but Ellen and the girls were certainly aware of the activities in the next room. Dorothy wondered how Henry would respond to her decision. They had not discussed that particular aspect in detail. Dorothy knew that Henry was aware that she had never been as amorous as he was, except for those first few months after her arrival. Four years later and with Mam and the girls in the house, she would be even less inclined to do her wifely duty. 'He will just have to adjust.' Dorothy had decided.

Chapter Twenty-Seven

Ellen and the girls settled into being in America quickly and Ellen found work at Shell's Laundry. Since she had past experience at the area dry cleaners in Leicester, she was hired immediately. Paula also found part time work at the Drug Store on the southwest corner of the town square, only a few blocks from the house and easily in walking distance. It was a popular hangout for the high school kids and Paula made many new friends. Working at the soda fountain was fun and Paula felt she would have loved being in Iowa if she hadn't missed Karl so much. They had settled their differences and started courting again briefly before she had left England. Paula had been writing letters, but Karl wasn't as fond of letter writing as she, and she began to miss him, even though Henry's nephew, Martin, showed an interest in Paula and they had shared a few evenings at the cinema.

Victoria wasn't old enough to go to work, so she spent her time helping Mam and Dorothy at home. She would be enrolled in school in the Fall, but she wasn't very happy about it. She was worried that things would be so strange from what she knew in school in England. She had been ready to take the exams for the next level back in Leicester, now she might have to take classes over to fit in at the American school, Mam had told her. Dorothy assured her that school in America wouldn't be that much different and that she would catch on quickly. "You're a bright girl, Victoria. What are you worrying about? You will make lovely new friends." Victoria wasn't so sure and her mood became more glum as the weeks went along. She enjoyed passing her time playing with Barbara, but disliked it when she had to be Barbara's care provider.

Dorothy felt that their life in America was going to be just fine, Mam and Paula had jobs and Victoria indeed became a big help with Barbara. So, within a few months of their settling in Dorothy found she was expecting her second child. She knew Victoria would be a tremendous help then too. Her life was now everything she could have hoped for.

Ellen worked hard at the laundry. It wasn't an easy job for a woman in her early fifties, and although she was tired at the end of the day, she knew that she had to help with the cost of groceries and utilities and other household expenses that were required to provide for such a large family, so she gave a portion of her earnings to Dorothy each pay period. Dorothy was pleased that things were going so well with her family being there.

Henry, on the other hand, was not so sure. It irritated him that even though Ellen helped with the groceries, she wanted to buy special things that only she liked. She didn't always stay on the budget that Dorothy had for grocery shopping and that angered him. Ellen particularly got on his nerves when she would buy **Maytag** blue cheese. Ellen had taken a great liking to the strong-smelling cheese and would buy it whenever she saw it in the grocery store if there was enough extra money and even sometimes when there wasn't.

Before their arrival, Dorothy had only shopped on Saturday afternoons. Henry got his paycheck on Friday and Dorothy shopped on Saturday. That routine worked well and Henry didn't mind taking Dorothy to the store, but with Ellen and the girls living there, shopping for that many people took more and the food and the budgeted money didn't always go as far as Dorothy had hoped.

One evening when Henry came home from work especially tired from a long day, he found he had to take Dorothy and Ellen grocery shopping. "I'm sorry, Henry, but we've run out of milk, bread, and cereal. We could use a few other household things as well. It does take quite a bit extra for everyone."

Even though he didn't want to go, neither Ellen nor Dorothy knew how to drive a car, so it was his responsibility to take them, regardless of how tired he was. They had to have the necessities. He just wished they had planned better, so he didn't have to go out on a work evening. He wanted to eat his supper and nap on the couch. It had gotten harder and harder to get in a nap with Barbara and Victoria running around. This evening he was even more tired than usual and his patience was already a little short. It had been a busy day at work crawling underneath the cars doing oil changes and the summer heat had made the garage extra warm and humid.

Henry waited in the car at the grocery store while the ladies shopped. Thank goodness, Paula and Victoria had stayed at home with Barbara. He tried to lay his head back and relax but the late summer heat filled the car. When their shopping seemed to take longer than he felt was necessary, he was getting agitated at having to sit there in the hot parking lot. When they finally came out of the store with several large bags of groceries, Henry was concerned as to whether the shopping budget would last for the week. He knew that Dorothy was good at handling the money, but he hoped Ellen had put in some extra.

When they got home, the ladies began unpacking the bags and Dorothy started supper. Henry went to stretch out on the living room couch for a quick nap before supper. As he laid down, Barbara wanted to do her favorite thing, to curl daddy's wavy brown hair around her fingers while he was on the couch and pin it with bobby pins. She loved his hair and it had become a regular evening ritual for them. Normally, Henry enjoyed the special time they shared, but, tonight he was hot and tired and when he had told her "No", she ran to the bedroom in tears.

"Victoria, would you see to Barbara?" Ellen called to her youngest daughter. "Oh, Mam, not again. Why do I have to see to Barbara just because she's being a spoiled brat?" Victoria moaned.

"Victoria, do as you are told, now!" Ellen's voice raised in pitch. Henry tried to drown out the crying and complaining, but was unable to get much rest. The commotion wasn't helping his irritability either. When Dorothy called him that supper was ready, he had just dropped off to sleep. The short nap had not been enough.

Ellen had been setting the table while Dorothy prepared the meal. When it was ready, she called the girls to come and Dorothy called Henry. Barbara was still whining over not getting to curl daddy's hair. Victoria was grumbling at her to shut up. Paula had just gotten a letter from Karl and was sulking in the corner of the kitchen table. When Henry walked into the kitchen Ellen was slicing up a big chunk of blue cheese.

"You're eating that stinking stuff again?" The long hot day and the noise in the house had gotten the best of him.

"Yes, I like it."

"But it smells like dirty socks."

"It's supposed to smell like that, it's blue cheese."

Henry turned to Dorothy and said, "Well, buy something that doesn't smell so bad. We don't need to spend the grocery money on that."

"I bought it with my own money." Ellen responded with a glare at Henry.

Henry had reached his limit. "I don't care whose money you used, I don't want that stinking stuff in the house!" he shouted. Henry grabbed the chunk of cheese off the table and threw it out of the back door of the kitchen. "There will not be any more of that smelly crap in this house, do you hear me?"

Ellen started to object, but Dorothy quickly shushed her mother. She wanted Henry to calm down so they could eat their supper in peace. Henry didn't get angry often, but when he did, he wasn't always able to control his temper. Dorothy had seen it on a few occasions. She thought about the time she had locked the door to the house when they had left to grocery shop and had failed to bring the key. In his anger, Henry had kicked in the back door breaking her favorite cookie jar on the kitchen table. When she had cried about it, Henry had stomped out of the house and didn't return for several hours. She knew that he was close to this evening's event escalating to that level and Ellen saying anything further would have only made it worse.

The meal was served and eaten in silence and Henry went to bed shortly afterwards. Ellen also retired to her own bedroom without a further word to anyone. The girls were quieter than they had ever been and Dorothy put Barbara down for the night early and she didn't even fuss. The atmosphere in the little house was tense.

They had managed to get through the rest of that night without incident, but it was not to be the only time Ellen and Henry were to butt heads.

Ellen was a plus sized woman and she liked to be stylish in spite of her size. She colored her hair a light blonde and wore dangly earrings in her pierced ears. She always had a brooch pinned to her blouse or jacket lapel. She had brought high-heeled shoes with her from England. She loved to wear them whenever she went out. The high-heeled shoes had been the latest thing after the war ended and Ellen had saved to buy them. Unfortunately, they had metal tips on the heels. Walking around the kitchen linoleum with those metal tips and the combination of her weight had put little indents in the flooring. When Henry saw the damage, he was beyond furious. He had spent a lot of money and many hours building the house and laying the linoleum only to have it ruined by Ellen and her high-heels. When Henry informed Ellen that she could not wear her heels in the house ever again, she had stomped out of the kitchen and into the bedroom once more.

Dorothy tried to reconcile these problems when they arose, but it was difficult with so many people living in their four small rooms. The Council house in Leicester hadn't been that much bigger, but Dorothy realized they had been family there. Here it was Dorothy and her family and Henry felt like he was the outsider in his own house.

Things were not easy for Paula and Victoria either. Paula cried a lot because she missed Karl. Victoria didn't like babysitting Barbara and complained a lot about it. When Ellen would correct her about her attitude, she would go to their bedroom and sulk. When Henry came home one evening after another long, busy day, Paula and Victoria were both in the bedroom crying. "What's wrong with them now?" Henry grumbled.

"Paula just got a letter from Karl and won't come out. Victoria has been complaining about Barbara again. Mam had to correct her. It's not been a good day here." Dorothy told him.

"So what exactly did Barbara do? She's only four and a half. She couldn't be that much of a problem. Victoria needs to stop complaining and do what she has to do to earn her keep here."

Ellen was just coming from the bathroom and heard this exchange. "What do you mean, earn her keep? I provide enough from my pay each week to cover our expenses. Paula helps out too and poor Victoria does get stuck with taking care of Barbara all the time. I tell my girls they need to do their part and be thankful for having this home, but they are young and feel like strangers here. They both are having a hard time adjusting. Dorothy, you don't feel the same way, do you?"

"Of course not, Mam. Henry is just tired and he wants to come home to a peaceful house. It's not been easy for him since you all came."

Henry just shook his head and mumbled as he walked away, "I never asked them to come."

When Ellen heard him, she turned to go after him. Knowing that would just lead to more problems, Dorothy gave Ellen a look and said, "Leave it, Mam." Ellen said no more that night.

But she didn't always keep her opinions to herself on other occasions. She was an outspoken woman and even though she loved Dorothy and liked Henry most of the time, the thought of them in the next bedroom doing "the nasty" was almost more than she could bear. It just brought back bad memories of Jack Parnell and his lustful ways. She didn't want that for her daughter. She knew from what she had been hearing regularly from the bedroom a few feet away, that Henry continued having his way as Dorothy did her wifely duties.

When everyone turned in for the night, the girls would drop off to sleep right away, but Ellen would often lie awake. The sounds of the birds, dogs barking, and the trains that went by every night kept her from getting much rest. It was so different from the sounds of Burfield Street.

For several weeks after their arrival, Dorothy had refused Henry's advances. She knew that the sound of their lovemaking would carry into the tiny room next to theirs. "Dorothy, I know that you wanted your family here, but I am your family now. I can't go on like this; I have my needs." Henry complained regularly.

"Yes, but Mam and the girls are right there." This conversation had become a constant argument over the ensuing months. Whenever he made advances, Dorothy would try to stall him off or at least try to keep the noise to a minimum. "Henry, shush, slow down a bit, Mam will hear you."

"They went to bed an hour ago and have been asleep long enough. Come on, Doe, show me some of that good old English lovin'." Henry thought if he teased her, maybe Dorothy would come around. "I miss you, Doe, this is our house and we can't even enjoy each other in it."

"Okay, but we need to be quiet enough so we don't wake them up." Dorothy said reluctantly.

"We've never woken Barbara up and she's in the same room as them."

Dorothy tried to remind him that Barbara was still a baby and slept soundly and wouldn't understand the sounds she might hear, but Mam and the girls were a different story. Henry was getting a bit upset and his voice reflected his growing anger. His decibel level had started to rise. Dorothy wanted to keep peace in the house, so when she finally agreed, she tried to keep him as quiet as possible.

In the next room Ellen laid awake listening to the sounds she knew so well. She didn't want to tell Dorothy that she could hear everything, but after several months of listening to those familiar grunts and groans, it brought back such unpleasant memories of her life with Jack, that she couldn't stand it any longer. She felt she had to say something, so the next morning she said, "Dorothy, luv, I don't mean to intrude on you and Henry's life, but I can hear you doing your wifely duty."

Dorothy was embarrassed. "Oh, Mam, I'm sorry. I'll try to keep Henry quiet and calmed down a bit. But remember how small this house is. I knew that curtain we hung in the doorway would give you some visual privacy but I know it doesn't do much to block the sounds. Please understand that it's important to Henry and I want him to be happy." Ellen just shrugged. 'What else could she say? All men were alike, they just wanted their pleasure.'

Later that evening in their bedroom Dorothy made the mistake of telling Henry what Ellen had said. Dorothy could see that Henry wasn't taking the news as she had hoped. She wanted him to understand and to curb his advances. "Well, she can just put a pillow over her head." Henry burst out in anger. "I told you this would be a problem when you said they were coming."

"I know, I know, sweetheart, but can we just try to do it a little less, just for Mam's sake. It is such a small house and they are right there in the next room. She is embarrassed by our lovemaking and I don't want to upset her."

"Upset her? UPSET HER? This is my house and I will make love to my wife any time I want." Henry's anger was coming to a boiling point and when Dorothy tried to shush him, it made him all the madder. To calm him down, Dorothy started kissing him and caressing him. It was the only thing she knew to do. Maybe it was because of their argument or maybe Henry was just being difficult, but regardless of the reason, their lovemaking that night was more arduous and louder than ever.

Afterwards, Henry was ready to go to sleep but before he even had time to roll over, Ellen's voice came loud and clear from the back bedroom, "Are you two done yet?"

"That's it, that's it, I won't put up with this in my house any longer!" Henry shouted and jumped out of bed. Alarmed at what he might do, Dorothy ran after him. "Henry, Henry, calm down. We knew this house was small and that sounds would carry. There's not much we can do about it."

"Oh, yes there is. I've put up with her meddling for over eight months now and that's long enough. They need to find their own place and I mean now!"

"But Henry, it's Winter. That's not a good time to be moving, and Christmas is coming."

"I don't care. They need to be out of this house." Henry had lost all of his patience and reasoning with him went to deaf ears. Dorothy knew she had to do something.

"Alright, alright, Mam and I will look for some place in the morning," Dorothy replied reluctantly. Henry grumbled and went to bed with his back turned away from her and Dorothy laid awake wondering how she would explain it to Mam. But she didn't need to say anything because in the morning at the breakfast table Ellen said, "The girls and I are going home. Paula misses Karl and Victoria misses her family and friends in England and I know we are in the way and not wanted here."

"Oh, Mam," Dorothy cried with tears welling up. "That's not true. You know how much I love you and the girls. I missed you so much when you were still in England and I was here. It's been wonderful having you with me. It's just that it is quite an adjustment for Henry. Have patience and we will work it out. Can you be just a little less antagonistic?"

"Antagonistic? What do you mean? If we are being antagonistic, we need to go."

"Mam, I didn't mean it the way it sounded. It's just that Henry wants his home back. I never realized how crowded it would be with all of us living here. I just wanted you with me so badly. Surely you can understand that. I'll help you find a place for you and the girls and Henry and I will help you move."

"And what will we do for furniture and household items? We don't have a stove or icebox. We don't even have dishes and pots and pans and I don't have the money to buy them. I don't earn that much at the laundry. Paula's little earnings from the soda fountain won't be much help."

"We can help you get those things. I'm sure Momma Collins and the family have some extra pots and pans they will let you use till you get settled."

"I think the best thing for us would be to return to England where we have all our own things. Your Da has written that he misses us and that he will change his ways if we come home. I've been thinking about it anyway. Paula cries every time she gets a letter from Karl. Victoria complains about caring for Barbara all the time. We've been here long enough and it's just not working. Your Da wants us to come back and he said he will send the money."

Dorothy hugged her mother with a heavy pain in her heart. And after just nine months in America, Ellen, Paula, and Victoria returned to England in early 1952.

Henry was happy to see them go and even though she was sad at their departure, Dorothy hoped that their lives would get back to normal now that they would have the house to themselves again and there would be peace in the Collins household. Well, at least until the new baby arrived.

Chapter Twenty-Eight

Deanna Joan Collins did arrive on May 21st of 1952. She was a much happier and more content baby than Barbara had been. Dorothy had quit smoking during her pregnancy and found that she felt better throughout it all, much better than the first time. She knew she should have stopped smoking then, but she never really smoked much. Since Henry smoked when they met, she had enjoyed having a cigarette when he offered one when they went out. She continued to enjoy an occasional one during an afternoon break from housework. Mam had also complained about both of them smoking inside the house and that again had been a bone of contention with Henry.

Dorothy had decided not to attempt to nurse Deanna for fear she would be fussy just like Barbara, so she put the new baby immediately on the Enfamil formula that old Doc Smith had suggested and Deanna flourished. She wasn't as pretty a baby as Barbara had been. She had bright red hair and a ruddy, flushed complexion, but she slept all night and was happy during the day, so peace did finally come to the Collins household again. Well, for Henry at least. Dorothy still missed Mam.

****

It had been over a year since Mam and the girls had returned to England. Barbara was attending Kindergarten classes three afternoons a week and even though Dorothy kept busy taking care of Deanna, her life seemed empty. She missed the sound of Mam and the girls' voices. She had been so happy to have them there and she was sad they had not seen the new baby. Dorothy had been a bit disappointed to have another girl. She had wanted a son to name David. She had learned the name David was from the Bible when she was young. She liked that it meant beloved. But when sweet little Deanna Joan joined the Collins household, she became a special delight to Dorothy. She was so different from temperamental, independent, Barbara.

Letters from Mam talked about how life was after their return. Paula was happy to be with Karl again and they were now engaged. Victoria enjoyed being with her friends again. She sat for the exams at school and Jack had promised they could pay for her to go on to the next levels if she wanted to. Ellen had written that life with Jack had been better at first, but lately she began talking more and more about his return to his old ways. He was as amorous as he had been in his younger days and Ellen wanted no part of it. Later, she knew that he found his comfort in other places and that suited them both fine. They could continue to live in the same house and live independent lives.

As Dorothy read the letters, she wanted more and more to see Mam again. She continued to put away the money in her savings envelope. She scrimped and saved more than she had before hoping to see her money grow even faster.

Henry hadn't realized until the spring of 1953 that Dorothy was planning to go home to England with the girls without him. She had not talked about it in quite a while and he thought Dorothy had let go of the idea of them taking the trip. Whenever Dorothy had approached a discussion of their going, Henry said he was too busy at work and besides it was too expensive. That had been the end of her talking about it. She seemed content with raising the girls. Barbara was close to finishing her first year in school and little Deanna was ten months old by this time. He didn't know that Dorothy had been faithfully filling her special envelope and making plans to go with just the girls. The sting of that last argument about Mam's leaving had remained on her mind for the past year. She felt she could get a job in England and stay with Mam and Da until she could find a place for herself and the girls. She loved Henry, but not being near her family had taken its toll on their marriage. She blamed him for losing her family.

After Ellen and the girls had left, Henry found a new job in the maintenance department at the aluminum window and door factory in town. Even though he was earning more money than he had as a garage mechanic, he still felt that saving money for a trip to England was a waste. He certainly didn't know how much Dorothy was stashing away in the cupboard. He never questioned her. He knew she was a good money manager and the bills were always paid in full and on time. There were more things he wanted to do with the house, but whenever they talked about it, it would end in an argument, and things between them continued to be tense. Their life was not as good as it had been when she had first arrived. The tension that started between them when Ellen and the girls were living with them had been slowly driving a wedge between them and things hadn't gotten much better since they left. Dorothy was depressed and blamed Henry for driving her Mam away. Henry would not apologize and the tensions continued to mount. Many more arguments ensued after they went to bed when Dorothy refused his advances.

Dorothy was concerned that Barbara was now old enough to hear and understand their arguments at night. She worried as to what kind of effect it would have on her young daughters if she and Henry continued arguing this way. Dorothy had made a special effort to keep their conversations for late in the evening after Barbara and Deanna had gone to sleep. But again, the small house with no doors between the rooms, made it easy for anyone to hear their conversation. Barbara had become a light sleeper and often heard her parents arguing in the next room. And although she tried to block it out, sleep eluded her as she heard their angry voices.

At breakfast one morning, Barbara asked, "Mommy, why are you and daddy talking so loud at night? Daddy sounds like he is mad at you. It makes me sad."

"Oh, sweetheart, it's just grown-up talk and sometimes we do get a little loud. Don't worry your pretty little head about it. We are talking about taking a big trip to visit your grandmother and aunts in England. Won't that be fun?"

"I don't know. I don't really remember them very much. Is England very far away? I don't want to leave Daddy."

Another argument began when Dorothy told Henry about Barbara's comments, "Henry, we need to stop arguing, the girls can hear and it worries them. I miss Mam and I need to see her and Barbara and Deanna need to know their British family. Barbara barely remembers her grandmother and they've never seen Deanna. If Mam and the girls were still here, I would be happy, but you saw to that."

"Oh, not this same old conversation. I don't know what you expected of me. I built this house for us and our children, not your mother and sisters."

"But you agreed to have them here."

"I didn't have much choice. You sent them our money without telling me. Then you were so excited about having them come and I knew they would need a place to stay while they found jobs and settled in, so I agreed to that. I just didn't think they would stay nine months! You know how we didn't have any privacy. Every time I went into the bathroom, one of the girls wanted in. And your mother didn't know when to keep her opinions to herself about our private time together."

"Henry, how can you be so cruel? I came all this way for you. I left my family and everything I ever knew to be with you. I thought you'd be happy for me to have some of my family with me. Now since you've ruined that, I'm going to go see them with or without you."

"Well, don't expect me to go with you. If I never see Ellen again, it won't upset me."

The arguments went on and on. Dorothy set about making her plans for the trip. She had their passport photos taken and applied for them. Henry became sullen and distant. His lovemaking had become rougher and when Dorothy finally refused him completely, he quit making any attempt and what was left of their closeness dwindled off with it.

Henry's constant thoughts were about the loss of his family. He knew that Dorothy intended to go to England and possibly would not be returning at all. That sweet pretty woman was leaving him and he wouldn't see his daughters grow up if things continued as they were, but he didn't know how to mend their relationship. Dorothy wanted her family and all he wanted was his and their stubbornness was pulling them apart.

Packing took several weeks as Dorothy prepared for herself, as well as a six-year-old and a baby in arms to make the long trip. She arranged for Barbara to leave Kindergarten in early March so they could spend the maximum amount of time with Mam before Barbara entered school full time. She told Henry she planned to stay several months, not returning until late Fall or early Winter of 1953, but in her heart she didn't know if she would be back at all. Henry was not happy that she planned to be gone so long, but she insisted the cost of the trip would not be worthwhile unless she had a good visit with her family. The thought that she might not return played heavily on both of them.

So with great sadness Henry loaded their things into the car and drove them to the train station. He wanted her to stay, but he knew there was nothing more he could say that would make her change her mind. There was no point in starting another argument that would linger in their memories on the day she was leaving.

He was too stubborn to admit to himself that he was losing them and should go with them. He couldn't bring himself to do more than think about it. Perhaps if I hadn't been so verbal about their going, maybe they would have wanted to come home again. How have things gotten so far out of hand? He was losing that sweet little woman he had loved since the moment he saw her.

"Dorothy, will you at least write like you did when we were first apart. I need to know how you and the girls are doing. I don't want you to stay six or seven months.

It's so long, Deanna will be all grown up. She'll be walking by the time you come back and she probably won't even know me. Oh, Doe why? I wish you wouldn't go." All the while Henry was talking he knew there was a good possibility he might never see his family again.

"You know I need to go." Dorothy pleaded one last time. "You could come with us. There is enough money for you too."

"I can't do that."

"Or you won't do that."

The argument was starting again and Henry turned away and nothing more was said as he loaded their luggage into the car. He was not going with them to New York. He had told her in a fit of anger that if she wanted to go so bad, she could make the trip alone. He worried about her and the children on the long train ride to New York all alone, but he stubbornly refused to change his mind. As he watched her struggle to board with Barbara and baby Deanna in her arms, he almost ran to beg her stay. But, at that moment, the Porter who had loaded the luggage, reached out and helped her step up so Henry turned away as the train pulled away from the station. He couldn't watch his reason for life leaving and as he drove home in tears, he knew that she might be gone for good.

Chapter Twenty-Nine

Knowing that she and the girls were to spend two days on the train to New York alone hadn't deterred Dorothy. It was scary traveling with two young daughters and all their things, but the knowledge that she would soon be home with Mam again kept her shoving any fears deep down inside. Her only thoughts were on getting to England and Mam. Henry couldn't stop her now.

They would board the **Queen Mary** in New York for the trip across the Atlantic. In her anticipation, Dorothy had thought the crossing would be like it was when she first came to America. During the excitement of planning the trip home to Mam, she hadn't given much thought to the difficulty of traveling with a six-year-old and a baby. She had only concentrated on how thrilled she was to be seeing her own family again and she placed everything else, including Iowa and Henry, at the back of her mind.

The **Queen Mary** was a passenger liner and much different that the **SS Argentina** troop ship seven years earlier. The cabins were larger and fitted out much nicer. Ellen had helped Dorothy make the arrangements through the T.B.P.A. club and that made it much easier, but the crossing did prove to be much more difficult than she had anticipated.

Deanna was teething and was quite fussy. To add to the problems, Barbara kept leaving the cabin to wander the corridors of the ship. She was bored staying in the cabin with the crying baby, so she would sneak out whenever Dorothy wasn't looking. Fortunately, the Porters were good to watch after her and guide her back. Deanna continued to cry a lot and Dorothy felt some seasickness since she couldn't spend as much time on deck getting fresh air. Deanna may have had a touch of seasickness as well, but Barbara's continuous wandering on deck had helped keep her from succumbing. Dorothy thanked the Lord for keeping Barbara safe and well. It would have been an even more horrible crossing if Barbara had joined in the chaos in the cabin! Throughout it all, the only thing that kept Dorothy sane was the knowledge that she was going to see her family again. Six or seven long months or longer to enjoy them! That thought was foremost in her mind, so she didn't realize she was pushing Henry further and further to the back.

How she managed to survive those two weeks aboard ship was a miracle. When she saw her Uncle Lawrence at the dock waving and smiling, she felt such relief that she began to cry. "Oh, Lawrence, you are a sight for sore eyes. Thank you so much for coming to get us. It's been a bit of a trial getting here."

"You needn't shed any more tears, luv, I've got the train tickets right here and my car is waiting at the Leicester Rail Station for us when we arrive. Ellen is busy getting the house ready and cooking your favorite things. She's been bustling about for days in anticipation. She can hardly contain herself." Lawrence chuckled. "I'll get us a cab while you gather your things."

Dorothy thought the train trip to Leicester seemed as long as the one from Iowa to New York. Ninety miles can feel like a thousand when your anticipation is high. Each little village they slowed through made the trip endless. 'Come on, hurry up, hurry up.' When the train finally arrived at the Leicester Rail Station, Lawrence couldn't get their things into his car quick enough for Dorothy. She was so anxious to see Burfield Street. As she looked out the car window, she felt the lovely brick buildings welcoming her home.

On the train Barbara wandered from her seat as she had aboard ship. Running up and down the aisle was disturbing the other passengers and Lawrence could see how flustered Dorothy was with the baby, so he thought he would try to help, even though he was a bachelor and had never particularly liked young children. He taught at the university where his students were older and anxious to learn, so his talents at coping with a six-year-old were limited. But because he knew it would help Dorothy relax, he called to her, "Barbara, come sit with me and tell me what you have learned in school. When we get to your grandmomma's in Leicester, I shall take you to see my school if you like." His voice was stern and direct and it sounded strange to Barbara's ears. She wasn't sure she wanted to sit with him.

When Barbara was hesitant, Dorothy gave her a nod. "Okay," Barbara said shyly. His British accent was so foreign to Barbara, a bit frightening. Mommy had said this might be their new home. 'Would everyone talk like that?' she wondered. 'Will I have to learn how to talk that way too? I won't go to his school if that's what I have to do!' Barbara made up her mind. 'I will sit and talk to him, but I won't go to school!' In spite of her first misgiving, Barbara did enjoy listening to Uncle Lawrence tell stories and the train ride flew by.

Ellen had been watching in anticipation at the window. When she saw Lawrence's car turn off Catherine Street, she ran out to meet them and to welcome Dorothy and the girls with open arms. In between sobs and hugs she said, "Oh my, Barbara, love, how much you have grown. And look at this little Deanna, what a lovely baby. How old is she now; did you say ten months?"

"Yes, Mam. She's trying to walk now and I'm sure she will be running by the time of her first birthday. Oh, what a joy it is to be home." Dorothy said as she hugged her Mam again.

Wiping the tears from her eyes and taking Deanna into her arms, Ellen said, "Dorothy, where did she get such red hair?"

"Isn't that funny, Mam? I don't remember anyone in our family with red hair. It must have come from Henry's side." That was the first thought she had had of Henry for weeks and for a moment a twinge of homesickness for him crossed her heart. But the joy of being with Mam again quickly wiped away any further thoughts of him and the little house in Iowa.

That is until his letters began to arrive. In every one he spilled out his love and sorrow at letting her go....

From Henry:

You are my dearest, the most wonderful woman in the whole world. Gosh, how I love you and here I am writing like I promised. I'll write twice a week and maybe if I find the time, I'll write more.

More from Henry:

Hello my sweet, this is Saturday night and I promised I would write. I didn't get a letter today. I wanted to hear from you so bad, but I guess I'll have to wait. Gosh, honey, I miss you so. I went to the show, but I couldn't enjoy it without you. I seemed lost sitting there all by myself. I saw a man kissing his wife in the picture and I wish I could do the same.

Boy, I wish you were here, it's just being with you that I care for, just to know you are alright and where I can look after you. Gosh, Honey, I love you so much. I'm crazy about you. I love you with all my heart. Remember, whatever happens I've always loved you and can't go on without you. As ever, your loving husband, Henry.

Dorothy's letters were newsy about the children and the rest of the family along with her brief expressions of love. But she was careful not to be too gushy for fear of upsetting Henry or making any definite promises as to when or if she might return. After all, he hadn't really apologized. So she kept the letters light.

From Dorothy:

My dearest, Remember the picture of us I have here? Well, when I say to Deanna, "Where's daddy", she looks right at it and says, "Da Da". It sounds so sweet.

Both of the children are fine. Lawrence took Barbara to town this morning and they went all round the market. Then this afternoon she went to the show with Cousin Malcolm and now she's out playing in the street. It's still light out and it's 8 o'clock. Deanna has another tooth at the top and she can eat like a little pig with it. I've cut out two bottles so she will be weaned before too long. She's walking and it's hard to keep her legs from getting sore because she's so fat. I bought her a pair of brown shoes today. They look quite nice.

Today was Mam's birthday. We celebrated with very nice flowers and nylons. The television set has been on the blink. The man came yesterday and we now have it on tonight.

Well, honey I'm out of things to say. I love you, but you should know that I do. I've always tried to make our marriage work. I know I've done without things and clothes when others have had everything. I don't mind just so long as you love me and the children.

Well, honey, I'll close for now, but take care of yourself and please don't worry. Love to Momma and Papa. Bye Bye, Love, Dorothy & Children.

From Henry:

Dearest Dorothy, my one and only, I finally got your letter and was sure glad to get it. I didn't know what to do with myself all day Saturday, but now that I got it, I'm not so sure I feel any better. You sound like you are getting more settled in now. Dorothy, I am not settled yet and I don't think I ever will be until you get home. I tell you I can't do anything and do it right. It seems I've got to have you here to keep me going.

I tried to take off the wallpaper like you had wanted, but it didn't work out at all. I gave up on it and went to bed at 8 o'clock. I just couldn't get you off my mind. Dorothy, if I ever as much let you go anywhere again for even one day, I'm going to shoot myself. I mean it, Doe, I'll never let you out of my sight again. You don't know what agony I have been in since you left and I tell you I can't stand it any longer. Remember, whatever happens, I have always loved you.

You've got your folks and all your old friends over there to keep you from thinking of me so much, but, I've got no one to help me out. You know mom and dad aren't any company. And I don't want to go out.

I can't go on alone, Dorothy, I've tried. Hell, I have tried, I thought I could do a few odd jobs, but I can't think when you're not here. I took a job laying linoleum, but I couldn't do it. Just somehow, I couldn't lay it straight and Les Davis fired me. I can't blame him. I just can't make things go my way, you're a part of me, Dorothy, so much a part of me, I can't do my work right at the shop, it seems everything goes wrong. Mr. Floyd would have understood that I'm not all there when you are so far away, but I have this new job to think of now. I feel like I'm going out of my mind. Sometimes I think I am. If I keep going down the way I am, there won't be anything left of me. I've lost 4 ½ pounds this last month. It's worrying over you because I love you so much. I do hope you will come home. Honey, do you really like it over there? Do you really want to stay? I've got to know.

Letter after letter Henry wrote expressing the agony he was feeling at her leaving him, so after three months of reading his letters and knowing how much he missed and needed her, Dorothy realized she missed Henry, her home and Momma and Papa Collins. She knew that they had become her family as well as Mam.

From Dorothy:

You said in your letter whatever happens remember I've always loved you. Oh, honey, what a thing to say when I am so far away. It makes me cry whenever I think of it. I couldn't stand it without you and what would the children do? We need you, my darling, so please look after yourself. We are coming home to you as soon as we can. Keep thinking about that, sweetheart. I promise we will never leave you again. I can't even get my "good" out of my visit knowing you are feeling so bad. I have seen them all and that's the main thing. I know it helps me to see my folks and friends, but it doesn't mean I think of you any less. Why darling, you are my whole life. You know, right from the start the way we met, we were meant for each other and darling, we will have many happy years together,

Henry was ecstatic to get this letter from her......

More from Dorothy:

Hello my dearest, Well, here is the news you have been waiting for, we sail for home on June 10th on the *Georgic*. It takes longer than the *Queens,* but I don't care, just so we get back to you. Mam and I went through Cooks Travel here in Leicester. I signed the papers and everything is finished and I just have to call in for our tickets and we will be sailing home to you. You are sure you will be in New York, won't you? I will let you know when we arrive in New York, probably around the 19th, but I will let you know for sure. Anyway, sweet, I am coming back to stay and that's all that matters, isn't it?

It had seemed like years instead of just a few months that they were gone. Henry was glad to have her and the girls home and he vowed to never let her go again.

"Oh, Doe, I can't believe it's really you. You look wonderful. The trip did you some good?"

"Yes, it was lovely, Henry. It was so good to see Mam and I did miss you and

Momma and Papa. Everyone sends their love and said to tell you to come with us next time." Henry ignored that suggestion and just held his family closer.

"Just look at my girls, how you have grown. Did you miss your daddy? Come give me a hug."

"Yes, daddy, I missed you so much," they cried as Barbara threw her arms around her daddy's neck and hugged him tight. Deanna was a bit hesitant at first, she had only been ten months old when they left, but she couldn't resist the man who showed such love in his voice and welcomed them with open arms. Besides Barbara was hugging him, so Deanna toddled towards him and was scooped up for a big hug. Henry knew he never wanted them to leave him again.

Dorothy didn't want to tell Henry just then that she was already planning on putting money in her savings envelope for another trip. She hoped she would be able to convince him to come with her next time. Maybe since he had missed her so much this time, he would be willing to make the trip with her. She didn't want to talk about it right now. She just wanted to hug him and kiss him. There would be lots of time to talk about it again.

Life began to fall into place in their little house again. Henry's disposition had tempered by Dorothy's leaving him and Dorothy had grown up a bit more and was able to handle her homesickness better. She had also learned that lovemaking was something to be shared lovingly between them with anticipation and not a wifely duty. Long talks with Mam had helped Dorothy understand why Ellen had felt that way with Da and that Dorothy's life with Henry needn't be the same. Things weren't always perfect back in Iowa but Henry had become more understanding of Dorothy needing her family and she became more of a warm loving wife to Henry. Dorothy continued to write her weekly letters to Mam and Ellen did the same. Dorothy's special savings envelope began to grow and she was sharing with Mam that she would like to make another trip. She wasn't quite ready to tell Henry as she didn't know if he was willing to commit to going with them. That would be a conversation for a later day and she truly hoped he would.

The trip to England in 1953 had been wonderful for Dorothy and the girls, but because of the letters from Henry pouring out his heart, Dorothy had found she missed him too, so she made a promise to Henry that she would not leave him again as long as she could see her family regularly. He did finally promise they could make more trips to England if she managed to save enough money. So, the 1953 trip was just the first of many trips to be made to England. Ellen also made many trips to Iowa over the years with help from Dorothy's special envelope. Paula and Victoria never came with her again and Ellen's trips were for only a couple of months at a time. Henry managed to tolerate the short inconveniences and it never became an issue between him and Ellen again.

After saving diligently, in 1960, Dorothy made her second trip to England, taking the girls to visit again for the entire summer. Her friend, Gertrude, whom she had met on board the **SS Argentina** when she first came to America, made the trip with them. It was Gertrude's first trip back and she was excited to see her family. Henry had again chosen not to go. He was always too busy with work. Dorothy wasn't angry this time, but knew she would miss him. She was the first to write.

From Dorothy:

My Dearest Sweetheart. It is Sunday morning so I'm going to write to you again. I mailed a letter out Friday at teatime so this one will get there right after. Will it help, honey, if I keep writing to you often until I get back there? I don't mind writing to you because you come first above everything else.

Even though Henry loved getting Dorothy's letter of encouragement, not being able to stand being alone any longer, he booked a flight to England. Dorothy was unbelievably surprised when he arrived. When the taxi pulled up to Burfield Street, he walked down the entryway to the kitchen door. Dorothy thought her eyes were playing tricks on her. She screamed and ran to throw her arms around his neck and kissed him with all the passion he had been missing.

"Henry, what are you doing here?" she asked breathlessly after their long kiss.

"I couldn't stand it any longer at home without you. The house just echoed everywhere. I would walk through the empty rooms and it just didn't feel right. I don't want to ever be without you and the girls again. Where are they? Did they miss me?"

They were playing cards with Granddad in the living room and Dorothy called to them, "Girls come see what a surprise I have for you."

"Surprise, what is it?" Eight-year-old Deanna called back.

"Well, you have to come to the kitchen. It's too large for me to carry to the living room, so come on."

"Coming, Mom." The girls echoed in unison. They couldn't' believe their eyes either when they saw their dad standing there with a smile on his face and his arms open wide. They ran into his arms and hugged him so long and hard he had to chuckle as he pried their arms from around his neck.

"Daddy, what are you doing here?"

"Well, I just missed you and your mom so much, I had to come see you."

Jack Parnell had followed the girls into the kitchen and welcomed Henry with, "Tom, what a surprise!" They shook hands and then hugged each other with a bit of manly embarrassment.

Dorothy's family welcomed him with open arms and Henry found he actually enjoyed being in England again and wondered why he had held out for so long. Henry and Dorothy spent the next few weeks going to places they had been when they were young. The Corn Exchange had closed, but they walked down to city centre and reminisced. They took long walks in Abbey Park and fed the ducks and swans on the water. They sat in the pavilion and drank tea. Everything reminded them of their courtship, how much they had been in love, the war years and, all the letters they had written. Henry told Dorothy that he had saved all of her letters to him. She was surprised and confessed that she had done the same. Laughing at their silliness, they agreed to put them in the old wooden box behind the bed. It could be fun to read them again sometime when they were old and grey.

Dorothy and Henry visited their dear old friends, Cath and Barney Kane. Dorothy and Cath had written letters to each other over the years and they still remained friends, more like sisters. Cath loved Barbara and Deanna and was disappointed that she still had no children. She told Dorothy that they were just as much in love as they had been during the war years, and Cath kept saying maybe one day they would be blessed with a child.

The time Dorothy and Henry spent together with her family and friends again was more enjoyable than Henry had ever imagined. He and Jack played cards and chatted for hours. Jack had mellowed in his old age and he and Ellen had come to terms with each other and the time Dorothy and Henry spent in their house was peaceful. Henry even came to love Ellen again, as long as he didn't have to live with her for a long period of time.

Dorothy realized that Henry's brothers and sisters and their families had become as close to her as her own family. Momma and Papa Collins were getting older and Henry reminded Dorothy that they would not be with them forever. Dorothy then realized how much she missed them. They had become such a special part of her life in America. Momma Collins had been there for her when she needed help and whenever she missed Mam, she would confide in Momma Collins. Yes, Dorothy had to admit that her life was truly in Iowa and not in Leicester anymore.

So, after a few weeks of visiting with family and friends, they returned to Iowa. They weren't able to travel together since Henry had come alone to join them. He was unable to get a ticket on their flight so he went to the airport with them and hoped to book one on the next flight out. Dorothy and the girls had flown by jet prop through the T.B.P.A. arrangements. Henry had seen them off at London's Heathrow Airport. He waited on standby for any flight he could get. As he waited, nervously checking the flights, he heard his name called over the loudspeaker. "Henry Collins, please report to Passenger Assistance Desk at Gate #28."

A flight was about to leave with a seat cancellation and Henry could have it if he wanted. It was a jet and cost more, but it landed in New York before Dorothy and the girls. Henry met them as they came off their plane! How funny for the girls to say goodbye to their dad in London and hello in New York! The jet had flown across the Atlantic faster than their jet prop and he beat them there. Dorothy was so happy that they were now able to make the train trip back to Iowa together as a family.

Henry was thrilled to have his family home again and Dorothy realized too that it was where she was meant to be. It had taken another separation for them to realize they were meant to be together. Oh over the years, of course, Henry and Dorothy occasionally had their disagreements like all husbands and wives, but nothing like before. Henry knew that Dorothy was still saving her money diligently every pay day. He knew if she was going to continue leaving him he would have to either learn to deal with living on his own for several weeks every few years, or make the decision to go with her. Dorothy never made another trip without him. Life in Iowa became a contented time as the girls grew up. They both graduated from school and married and started their own families and Dorothy and Henry remained in the little white house with the red roof and as the old saying goes, "lived happily ever after."

Epilogue

As Barbara read the letters her parents had written so long ago, her thoughts wandered on how her life was so intertwined with theirs. She loved them both and the stories of their lives had become a part of hers. As she grew up and became her own person, she and Dorothy didn't always agree with each other, but their love never diminished. Dorothy had disapproved of Barbara marrying at age eighteen. Ellen Parnell must have felt the same way when Dorothy said she was going to marry her American serviceman and go to America with him.

Later when they found out Barbara was pregnant at age nineteen, Dorothy and Henry were extremely upset at her being so young. They had forgotten that Dorothy gave birth soon after she began her life in America! Their lives weren't so very different.

Dorothy had always called Barbara the strong, temperamental, independent one. Many times Barbara had resented that and their relationship had suffered in Barbara's younger years. But, the time Barbara spent with her mom during Dorothy's final months washed away all those differences, and her last days were the most precious ones to Barbara. Being the strong, temperamental, independent one became a blessing to them as they dealt with Dorothy's Alzheimer's.

Reading their letters, Barbara wondered why there were no letters between Dorothy and Grandma Parnell saved in that old wooden box behind the bed. The way Dorothy had always talked about her love for her mother, it seemed strange that she hadn't saved any letters from her. Of course, the love between a mother and daughter is quite different from the love between a husband and his wife so far away. You see, Henry had poured out his heart in every letter and that must have been more important. Barbara realized that even though Dorothy loved her Mam, she loved Henry more.

Over the years, Dorothy and Gertrude had continued to share their friendship. Gertrude's husband had turned out to be as good a husband as Dorothy's. He worked hard and provided for his family. They had a lovely home and two daughters. The two couples would spend many weekend evenings visiting. They lived in neighboring towns. Funny, when they had talked about possibly seeing each other when they arrived in Iowa, they had not realized how close they would really be. When Gertrude had made the trip to England with Dorothy in 1960, it made the trip so much better. Dorothy wished Gertrude had made the trip in 1953 when the girls were young. It would have made that trip so much easier too. Gertrude was happy for Dorothy when Henry finally joined them. She had been a little sad that her husband did not do the same, but knew that he couldn't get away from his farm duties as easily. Once Henry arrived, Gertrude and Dorothy's plans changed. When Henry had to return sooner because of work, Dorothy and the girls went with him. Gertrude decided to stay on in England a bit longer and while there were no words of disagreement about Dorothy leaving, their friendship diminished after that and they slowly drifted apart.

Henry and his best friend, Joe, had promised to stay in touch with each other after the war ended. They had become like brothers during their tour of duty together. They had often spoken of their friendship meaning so much to them. So, they did write for a while, but finally lost touch with each other over the years, as their lives changed. North Carolina was a long way from Iowa and their families were quite different.

Henry Collins died on December 14, 1979 at the age of sixty. He had lived fifteen months after his diagnosis of a cancerous brain tumor. Dorothy was only fifty-four at the time and until the day he died, she never gave up hope that he would make a full recovery and be her loving husband again. Those fifteen months were both long and short at the same time for everyone. Everyone wanted him to live, but not the way he was after the surgery. He could no longer walk unaided, nor dress himself or feed himself. His personality changed and they missed the fun loving, teasing husband and father he had always been.

During his last days, Dorothy rented all the equipment she would need and placed the hospital bed in the front bedroom where they had slept for more than thirty years. Henry could see outside the front window from his bed and watch cars go by as the seasons changed. Dorothy moved the living room furniture around so he had an unobstructed view of the television where he would spend his days watching shows he had never been able to watch during the years he had worked to support his family.

Dorothy applied for Henry's Social Security disability, which was their only income, but her money managing skills served her well. She moved her own bed into the back bedroom since their small bedroom could not accommodate both her bed and the hospital bed. She had always slept close to him, so she never got much sleep without him beside her. During those last few months she learned so much while taking care of him that upon his death she took training for a job as a nurses' aide at the community's small hospital, where she worked until she retired.

She never lost her love for her home in England and had grieved deeply when she lost her Mam, but continued to make the trips to see the rest of her family. Over the years her dark brown hair turned to shiny, silver grey but she never lost her petite figure and winning smile even after the Alzheimer's took over. She had adamantly refused to meet or go out with any other man, even though she had many potential suitors. She said no one could replace the love she had with Henry and she took that love to her grave on April 18, 2008 at the age of eighty-two.

In spite of all their differences, what Dorothy and Henry had was genuine, something so rarely found. It lasted through trials and triumphs, time and distance, laughter and tears. Their letters reflected their love for each other and the joy they shared. Their marriage had a strong bond that continued in spite of those conflicts throughout their thirty-four years of marriage. They dealt with their sorrows and raised a family in the little house that Henry had built for them. They had shared a love that had spanned the miles, the years, and beyond.

And that old wooden box? It still holds Dorothy and Henry's letters tied in the bundles with string. And even though it now lives behind Barbara's bed, its duties remain the same, keep safe all the treasures placed inside.